WHAT IF MORE IS POSSIBLE?

REAL JESUS

WHIT GEORGE

CHURCH ON THE MOVE

WORKBOOK IN 10 SESSIONS

TABLE OF CONTENTS

INTRODUCTION

I grew up going to church. I grew up reading the Bible (occasionally). I grew up knowing about Jesus. And as far as I knew, I was doing it right. I was a Christian, and that was alright by me. In fact, it was more than alright, I was happy about it. I felt good about myself. I really believed that I was one of the "good people" and that if the rest of world would just believe and behave a little bit more like me, well, then the world would be a better place.

The problem was that underneath the sheen of my external behavior was a heart that was very far from God. I liked God, but I *loved* me! God was a part of my life, you might even say He was a big part, but He was not at the center. I was.

The Jesus we encounter in scripture, the *real* Jesus, was so much more than an assistant for your life. He was so much more than a hero to admire or a teacher that you emulate so that you can be better at life. He is the very power that created the universe. He is the center of all things, and the one for whom all things exist. That was not the Jesus I knew.

Here in Tulsa, Oklahoma, where I live, lots of people know about Jesus. In fact, lots of people would tell you that they love Jesus. They cry every Easter, they have several Bibles in their homes and scriptures hanging on their walls as decor. Jesus is a big part of their lives, but He is not the center. And that's why we created the Real Jesus curriculum: to introduce people to the *real* Jesus.

So here's my question for you: What if there's more? What if Jesus is so much bigger than you think He is? Better than you think He is? More loving than you think He is? More gracious than you think He is? What if there's a joy and a peace available to you that you never thought possible?

Can I tell you, there is, and it's all found in the *real* Jesus.

So I invite you to leave all your preconceived ideas about who Jesus is right here, don't take them any further. Open your mind and your heart and ask Him to reveal Himself to you, because I can promise you, He will.

WHIT GEORGE
LEAD PASTOR OF CHURCH ON THE MOVE
JULY 2018

HOW TO USE THIS BOOK

Welcome to your Real Jesus small group experience. Over the course of the next several weeks we're going to walk through 10 sessions together, discovering what happens when a person meets the *real* Jesus.

Each of these sessions is centered around *encounters with Jesus*. We also engage with *words of Jesus* and their implications for our lives here and now. We have arranged each session into three major headings:

- Pre-Group
- **Group Time**
- Next Steps

Of these three, the only *essential* content for a great group experience is *Group Time*—you will grow if you engage with your group each week. That said, your personal investment in *Pre-Group* (about 45 minutes) will make each session come alive, not only for you, but for everyone else in your group. Lastly, consider *Next Steps* as a resource to help you find practical ways to put your faith into action.

PRE-GROUP

DO THIS ON YOUR OWN THROUGHOUT THE WEEK LEADING UP TO GROUP TIME.

We estimate 45 minutes needed for your *Pre-Group* work, depending on the individual. With each session we provide a Reading Assignment — a chosen passage of scripture to meditate on in preparation for that week's *Group Time*. With each Reading Assignment will be an opportunity for you to journal your Personal Reflections. And the last portion of *Pre-Group* will be a couple of Questions to Consider.

- Reading Assignment
- Meditation Moments
- Personal Reflections
- The Big Idea
- Personal Prayer Time

Pray honest prayers and expect God to speak to you through your Pre-Group reflections and He will!

GROUP TIME
DO THIS TOGETHER AS A GROUP.

Group Time is the heart of this *real* Jesus experience—you will grow as you engage! Here's how *Group Time* breaks down:

- Opening Thoughts
- Growing Connected
- Video Teaching
- Group Discussion
- Group Prayer Time

Your group leader (or someone assigned from your group) will read the Opening Thoughts section aloud and introduce the topic for that session. After that, everyone will have an opportunity to briefly share their own perspectives on the topic at hand, lead by the questions given in the Growing Together section.

You'll watch a 10–12 minute video teaching from Pastor Whit George. Finally, the Group Discussion that follows may be the most meaningful part of your time together.

> *What's most personal is what's most universal. Your willingness to share may be a catalyst to someone else's freedom as well as your own.*

NEXT STEPS
DO THIS INDIVIDUALLY AFTER YOU'VE MET WITH YOUR GROUP.

James 1:22 challenges us to "Be *doers* of the Word and not hearers only, deceiving yourself." That's the heart of this last section. After prayerful consideration and healthy, candid discussion, we want to help you take your next step. This section is intended to help lead you to what those steps might be.

Here are the resources available in each *Next Steps* section:

- Personal Challenge

- Helpful Questions

- Further Reading

> *When we take a step to do what only we can do,*
> *God does what only He can do in us.*

RECOMMENDED GUIDELINES

Here are some ideas to consider in order to make the most of your *Group Time*.

PERSONAL PREPARATION HELPS EVERYONE

Come prepared to each group session. It not only makes the content come alive for you, but it sharpens everyone around you. At best, preparation means working through the *Pre-Group* section before you arrive and coming ready to engage. At a minimum, preparation means praying for your group and bringing your Real Jesus book with you.

SPEAK FOR YOURSELF

During group discussion everyone benefits from your honesty and vulnerability. Make it personal with "I" statements. You're an expert on yourself more than anyone (including your spouse). E.g. "I know I struggle with _____" is better than "Everyone has an issue with _____" or "You seem to have an issue with _____".

BE COMFORTABLE WITH SILENCE

Some people are uncomfortable with silence. "This is group discussion time, shouldn't we be discussing?" It's okay to allow for silence between responses or to give someone time to express what they're feeling without interruption. Also remember— there is no pressure to share.

PUNCTUALITY IS THE BEST!

One of the best ways to honor your group is simply by showing up on time. Make every effort to be punctual and your group will appreciate it!

STRICTLY CONFIDENTIAL

What someone shares inside the privacy of your group is not to be shared outside the group. *Group Time* is a "brave space". Protect that by staying committed to not repeat what you hear.

SESSION ONE
REAL HOPE

PRE-GROUP

THE BIG IDEA

Jesus is *different* than you think He is and He offers *more* than you think He does.

WHO IS JESUS, REALLY?

"He was in the beginning with God."

JOHN 1:2 ESV

Jesus is different than you think He is. This is the point of the first chapter of John's Gospel. John, the author, (not to be confused with John the Baptist of whom he wrote) was not only one of Jesus' 12 disciples, he had been in Jesus' innermost circle of three. John saw Jesus do things not everyone got to see. He followed Jesus to places not everyone got to go and experienced things not everyone got to experience. John referred to himself as "the disciple Jesus loved."

About 40 years after the events of Jesus' ministry took place (circa 70 A.D.), John picked up his pen to write down his good news account. The very first thing John wanted to communicate was just how different Jesus was than he expected. Looking back at his time with Jesus, John realized that Jesus was so much more than even he knew.

Check out John's claims in just his first two verses! He takes readers to an expansive, cosmic view of eternity past and makes a staggering declaration. Not only does John say that Jesus was "there in the beginning with God" (verse 2), but he claims that Jesus was God Himself (verse 1).

What expectations are you bringing to your Real Jesus journey? Do you want Jesus to restore a relationship? Do you want Him to heal your body? Do you want Him to rescue your finances? Do want Jesus to free you from addiction? Do you want Him to make you wise? Do you want Jesus to give you purpose and direction? What if this journey is different than you thought it would be? What if Jesus is offering something more than any of those things?

Before John takes us through the narrative of what Jesus said and did, he wants us to consider who we're dealing with. From the start, John's claim is this—Jesus is not just a good teacher and a benevolent rescuer. Jesus is God.

COME AND SEE

Jesus turned and saw them following and said to them, "What are you seeking?" And they said to Him, "Rabbi (which means Teacher), where are you staying?" He said to them, "Come and you will see."
JOHN 1:38-39 ESV

Jesus offers more than you think He does. As you read through the narrative passages of John chapter one, you may notice that when Jesus called His disciples to follow Him, He wasn't always the one doing the calling. In fact, John the Baptist was the one who first sent his own disciples to follow Jesus (verses 35–37).

Notice what didn't happen when Jesus saw them approaching. He didn't say, "Good job, guys. You did it! You found Me. Let's get started." No, He stopped and asked a question meant to locate their hopes—"What do you want?"

It's as if Jesus is asking, "What hopes does following Me represent to you?" "What expectations do you have of Me?" Their answer is underwhelming. "Where are you staying?" Still Jesus compels them to follow, "Come and you will see."

Later in John 1, another disciple gets a call to follow Jesus from the testimony of a friend. Philip convinces Nathanael to come investigate this man Jesus, in spite of Nathanael's skepticism.

Nathanael was the kind of person who didn't take anything at face value. He wasn't easily impressed. We don't know if this was simply an expression of Nathanael's natural temperament or if he had just experienced enough reality to want to protect himself from seeing his hopes dashed by disappointment again.

Whatever the case, Jesus immediately lifted Nathanael's hopes. "Behold, an Israelite in whom there is no deceit!" (verse 47). Nathanael asked, "How do you know me?" Jesus tells Nathanael He saw him before his interaction with Philip.

What did that mean? We don't know. But apparently Nathanael did. Whatever it was, it must have been deeply personal to Nathanael. He immediately dropped his skepticism and proclaimed the divinity and saving power of Jesus. What a turnaround!

Still, Jesus wasn't done lifting Nathanael's hopes of who He is and what He offers. "You will see greater things than these," Jesus says (verse 50). "You will see heaven opened, and the angels of God ascending and descending on the Son of Man." (verse 51)

What hopes are you bringing to Jesus? Can you dare believe in something greater? Have you considered how limited your hopes may be? How could they not be? Our hopes are restrained by our personal experience, our knowledge of God, and our limited imaginations.

Yet, Jesus doesn't point out our smallness to shame us or to put us in our place. He simply wants us to begin to see Him in His. Jesus is God. Salvation is not just what He can give, it's who He is! Jesus offers us so much more than we expect. He offers Himself. Are you willing to come and see?

NOTES

BIBLE READING & MEDITATION

Grab a real paper Bible so that you can write in the margins, highlight verses, and make it your own. Read the following passages, meditate what you've read, and jot down your personal reflections.

DAY ONE

READ.

In the beginning was the Word, and the Word was with God, and the Word was God. He was in the beginning with God.
JOHN 1:1-2 ESV

And the Word became flesh and dwelt among us, and we have seen His glory, glory as of the only Son from the Father, full of grace and truth.
JOHN 1:14 ESV

REFLECT.

- What does this tell me about God?
- What does this tell me about myself?
- How would this change my life if I took it seriously?

WRITE.

DAY TWO

READ.

All things were made through Him, and without Him was not any thing made that was made.
JOHN 1:3 ESV

When I look at Your heavens, the work of Your fingers, the moon and the stars, which You have set in place, what is man that You are mindful of him, and the son of man that You care for him?
PSALM 8:3-4 ESV

REFLECT.

- What does this tell me about God?
- What does this tell me about myself?
- How would this change my life if I took it seriously?

WRITE.

DAY THREE

READ.

In Him was life, and the life was the light of men. The light shines in the darkness, and the darkness has not overcome it.

JOHN 1:4-5 ESV

For God, who said, "Let light shine out of darkness," has shone in our hearts to give the light of the knowledge of the glory of God in the face of Jesus Christ.

2 CORINTHIANS 4:6 ESV

REFLECT.

- What does this tell me about God?
- What does this tell me about myself?
- How would this change my life if I took it seriously?

WRITE.

DAY FOUR

READ.

Jesus Christ is the same yesterday and today and forever.

HEBREWS 13:8 NIV

Therefore God exalted Him to the highest place and gave Him the name that is above every name, that at the name of Jesus every knee should bow, in heaven and on earth and under the earth.

PHILIPPIANS 2:9-10 NIV

REFLECT.

- What does this tell me about God?
- What does this tell me about myself?
- How would this change my life if I took it seriously?

WRITE.

DAY FIVE

READ.

Nathanael answered Him, "Rabbi, You are the Son of God! You are the King of Israel!" Jesus answered him, "Because I said to you, 'I saw you under the fig tree,' do you believe? You will see greater things than these." And He said to him, "Truly, truly, I say to you, you will see heaven opened, and the angels of God ascending and descending on the Son of Man."

JOHN 1:49-51 ESV

"Call to Me and I will answer you, and will tell you great and hidden things that you have not known."

JEREMIAH 33:3 ESV

REFLECT.

- What does this tell me about God?
- What does this tell me about myself?
- How would this change my life if I took it seriously?

WRITE.

GROUP TIME

OPENING THOUGHTS

After a time of introductions or catching up, open with prayer and give everyone an opportunity to share their thoughts on this week's topic.

Use the Big Idea and Starter Questions below to open discussion and encourage people to reflect on their Pre-Group study. An easy way to do that is to ask about personal observations, pressing questions, or unique insights from this week's study.

GROWING CONNECTED

THE BIG IDEA

Jesus is different than you think He is and He offers more than you think He does.

STARTER QUESTIONS

1. How do you think Jesus is different than most people think? What kinds of hopes and expectations do people bring to God?

2. We've all been invited on this Real Jesus journey together. Who invited you to be a part of this and what made you say yes?

3. If you could ask Jesus for anything, what would it be?

VIDEO TEACHING

Write down any thoughts or ideas that stand out to you from this week's teaching.

DISCUSSION QUESTIONS

1. Would you say you're more of a "high hopes" person or more of a "realist"? Explain.

2. What are your honest expectations for this Real Jesus small group?

3. What are your highest hopes for this Real Jesus small group?

4. Tell about a time you felt disappointed in God because He didn't do what you expected.

5. Tell about a time you had an experience where God did something greater than you imagined He would.

6. What hopes or expectations would you find difficult to surrender?

GROUP PRAYER REQUESTS

NEXT STEPS

The Gospel of Mark chapter 1 says the fishermen Jesus encountered "…immediately left their nets and followed Him." What was it about Jesus that so compelled those fishermen to follow Him? They must have seen something in Him that captured their imaginations. They left everything they had previously hoped in (friends, family, career, comfort, etc.) to put the full weight of their hope in Jesus.

Your spiritual exercise this week is called "What Am I Really Hoping For?" In one page or less, write out all the current things you tend to put your hope in and why. Use these questions as a guide.

- What am I hoping to have in the future that will make me feel safe?

- What am I hoping to do in the future that will make my life more meaningful?

- What am I hoping will happen in my relationships that will make me feel affirmed?

- What am I hoping won't happen in my future that could ruin my plans?

- What am I hoping God won't ask me to do?

- What am I hoping God will ask me to do?

WHAT AM I REALLY HOPING FOR?

REAL WORSHIP

PRE-GROUP

THE BIG IDEA

Whatever has your heart has you.

WHO IS JESUS, REALLY?

Disheartened by the saying, he went away sorrowful,
for he had great possessions.

MARK 10:22 ESV

Most people tend to have a fairly binary view of worship. We worship or we don't. When we attend weekend church services we turn our worship setting from "Off" to "On." Then we clap, sing, lift our hands, and some of us even sway to the rhythm. That's worship, right? It's an outward expression we can choose as a way of honoring God.

Jesus doesn't seem to see worship this way. Throughout the Gospels, Jesus shows us that worship is not just external. It's deeply internal. "You worship what you do not know," He says (John 4:22). He seems to view worship as a wild, irrepressible force at work at the very core of your being. Whether you can see it or not, whatever has your heart has you.

One of Jesus' disciples recorded a story of a rich young ruler who approached Jesus asking for spiritual advice (Mark 10). From the very start, the man showed honor to Jesus. He bowed down to worship Him. He praised Jesus with words of affirmation by calling Him "good." This looked and sounded a lot like worship. The problem is, it wasn't.

Jesus saw right through the rich young ruler's outward expression and looked right into the man's heart. "Why do you call Me good?" Jesus said (Mark 10:18). Jesus wasn't trying to shame the man for his superficial display. Instead the Bible says, "He looked at him, and loved him..." Jesus gently reveals the true condition of his heart.

"You lack one thing: go, sell all that you have and give to the poor, and you will have treasure in heaven; and come, follow Me." This is not a prescription Jesus gave to everyone. Like a skilled surgeon, Jesus carefully diagnosed this man's condition—His heart belonged to another. His true worship was being given to something that would inevitably let him down. And he's trapped by his own wealth. Still, Jesus showed the way of escape.

One of the most tragic verses in all of scripture follows. "Disheartened by the saying, he went away sorrowful, for he had great possessions" (verse 22). Jesus loved him enough to tell him the truth about the condition of his heart. Yet the man walked away disheartened.

Whatever has your heart has you. Jesus loves our songs, our lifted hands, and our declarations of honor. But worship is so much more than that. Jesus wants your heart!

THE POWER OF WORSHIP

Jesus looked at them and said, "With man it is impossible,
but not with God. For all things are possible with God."
MARK 10:27 ESV

The disciples of Jesus were "exceedingly astonished." If this
Rich Young Ruler wasn't capable of eternal life, then who possibly
could be? Jesus took this opportunity to teach His disciples about
the power of worship.

"How difficult it is to enter the Kingdom of God," He said. Most
religious people of Jesus' day thought of health, financial success,
and influence as signs that God was pleased with you. Jesus
wanted to help His disciples see things differently. This man
turned his back on eternal life because of his health, financial
success, and influence.

"Then who can be saved?" they asked (verse 26). Now Jesus looks
at His disciples and loves them. "With man it is impossible,
but not with God. For all things are possible with God." Jesus
wanted them to see the power of a new affection. Loving Jesus,
surrendering your deepest longings to Him is the only thing
powerful enough to dislodge their grip on you.

What comforts you? What gives you identity? What relieves
you from anger, stress, boredom, loneliness, and emptiness?
What feels impossible to face life without? Could it be that those
things are the center of your worship? Whatever has your heart
has you. Jesus offers a path. Only He can dislodge your heart
from that which will inevitably let you down.

NOTES

NOTES

BIBLE READING & MEDITATION

Grab a real paper Bible so that you can write in the margins, highlight verses, and make it your own. Read the following passages, meditate what you've read, and jot down your personal reflections.

DAY ONE

READ.

"Do not lay up for yourselves treasures on earth, where moth and rust destroy and where thieves break in and steal, but lay up for yourselves treasures in heaven, where neither moth nor rust destroys and where thieves do not break in and steal. For where your treasure is, there your heart will be also."

MATTHEW 6:19-21 ESV

"Teacher, which is the great commandment in the Law?" And He said to him, "You shall love the Lord your God with all your heart and with all your soul and with all your mind."

MATTHEW 22:36-37 ESV

REFLECT.

- What does this tell me about God?

- What does this tell me about myself?

- How would this change my life if I took it seriously?

WRITE.

DAY TWO

READ.

"Yet a time is coming and has now come when the true worshipers will worship the Father in the Spirit and in truth, for they are the kind of worshipers the Father seeks."

JOHN 4:23 NIV

"Teach me Your way, Lord, that I may rely on Your faithfulness; give me an undivided heart, that I may fear Your name. I will praise You, Lord my God, with all my heart; I will glorify Your name forever."

PSALM 86:11-12 NIV

REFLECT.

- What does this tell me about God?

- What does this tell me about myself?

- How would this change my life if I took it seriously?

WRITE.

DAY THREE

READ.

Since then we have a great high priest who has passed through the heavens, Jesus, the Son of God, let us hold fast our confession. For we do not have a high priest who is unable to sympathize with our weaknesses, but one who in every respect has been tempted as we are, yet without sin. Let us then with confidence draw near to the throne of grace, that we may receive mercy and find grace to help in time of need.

HEBREWS 4:14-16 ESV

Create in me a clean heart, O God, and renew a right spirit within me. Cast me not away from Your presence, and take not Your Holy Spirit from me.

PSALM 51:10-11 ESV

REFLECT.

- What does this tell me about God?

- What does this tell me about myself?

- How would this change my life if I took it seriously?

WRITE.

DAY FOUR

READ.

Jesus said to him, "If you can believe, all things are possible to him who believes." Immediately the father of the child cried out and said with tears, "Lord, I believe; help my unbelief!"

MARK 9:23-24 NKJV

Incline my heart to Your testimonies, and not to selfish gain! Turn my eyes from looking at worthless things; and give me life in Your ways.

PSALM 119:36-37 ESV

REFLECT.

- What does this tell me about God?

- What does this tell me about myself?

- How would this change my life if I took it seriously?

WRITE.

DAY FIVE

READ.

Peter began to say to him, "See, we have left everything and followed You." Jesus said, "Truly, I say to you, there is no one who has left house or brothers or sisters or mother or father or children or lands, for My sake and for the gospel, who will not receive a hundredfold now in this time, houses and brothers and sisters and mothers and children and lands, with persecutions, and in the age to come eternal life."

MARK 10:28-30 ESV

"You will seek Me and find Me, when you seek Me with all your heart."

JEREMIAH 29:13 ESV

REFLECT.

- What does this tell me about God?
- What does this tell me about myself?
- How would this change my life if I took it seriously?

WRITE.

GROUP TIME

OPENING THOUGHTS

After a time of introductions or catching up, open with prayer and give everyone an opportunity to share their thoughts on this week's topic.

Use The Big Idea and Starter Questions to open discussion and encourage people to reflect on their Pre-Group study. Ask about personal observations, pressing questions, or unique insights from this week's study.

GROWING CONNECTED

THE BIG IDEA

Whatever has your heart has you.

STARTER QUESTIONS

1. In our culture, what things do people give their hearts to, besides God? How can you tell what has someone's heart?

2. What are some things people are most inclined to pursue to find satisfaction?

3. What kinds of things did your family seem to value most when you were growing up?

VIDEO TEACHING

Write down any thoughts or ideas that stand out to you from this week's teaching.

DISCUSSION QUESTIONS

1. What was your understanding of worship before today?

2. The Rich Young Ruler's possessions were the hardest thing for him to give up. What would be something difficult for you to give up?

3. Tell about a time you experienced a meaningful moment of surrender in your life.

4. Have you ever faced a habit that seemed impossible to overcome? Explain.

5. Tell about a time when God intervened in a situation that seemed impossible.

GROUP PRAYER REQUESTS

NEXT STEPS

The old English word for worship was worth-ship. As if to say, worship is ascribing worth to someone or something that's worthy of worship. Jesus wasn't telling the Rich Young Ruler that his life of influence, wealth, and good deeds were worthless. Jesus was showing him that those things were worth less than Him. It's usually not that we love the wrong things. It's that we love things in the wrong order. Jesus wants to give us the desires of our hearts, but only when we find our deepest satisfaction in Him.

Your exercise this week is to make a Worth-ship List. Use the next page to write out all the current things you value most in this life. This list of questions can help guide you.

- Who or what do I turn to for comfort?

- What am I known for? Where do I find my identity?

- What relieves me of stress, anger, and worry?

- Where do I turn when I'm bored or lonely?

- Where does my mind drift when things get quiet?

- What motivates me?

- What's something I can't live without?

MY WORTH-SHIP LIST

-
-
-
-
-
-
-
-
-
-
-
-
-
-
-
-

REAL SIN

PRE-GROUP

THE BIG IDEA

Sin is not just an external action, it's an internal condition.

WHO IS JESUS, REALLY?

"Woe to you, teachers of the law and Pharisees, you hypocrites!
You clean the outside of the cup and dish, but inside they are
full of greed and self-indulgence."

MATTHEW 23:25 NIV

There are two basic ways most of us deal with the problem of sin. The first is to take control of your life by being a rebel. Follow your heart. Make your own path. Just act as if there is no such thing as sin. If it feels good, do it. Eat drink and be merry, for tomorrow we die!

If this sounds like good old-fashioned hedonism to you, well that's because it is. Pursue happiness at all costs. Guilt is just an illusion. You be you. And if that also sounds like modern Western culture to you, well that's because it is. In Jesus' day, the rebels who lived this way were called "tax collectors and sinners."

There are all kinds of problems with this sin philosophy, though. Unrestrained pleasure has severe diminishing returns and leads to hopelessness, depression, and addiction. Maybe the worst thing that can happen to a person is that they get everything their impulsive heart desires. Still, Jesus had great compassion on those hopeless rebels who were honest about their sin.

The second way you may tend to deal with the problem of sin is to take control of your life by keeping the rules. The logic goes something like this: Rules are good. Good people follow the rules. I follow the rules. I'm good.

It's true, though, isn't it? Life does tend to reward well-behaved, high achievers. The people who understand the rules and keep them well often find themselves in positions of power and authority. In Jesus' day, these people were called "scribes and Pharisees."

Scribes and Pharisees actually love the concept of sin. It's useful to them. They see themselves as standing outside of it. The problem is, they're not. The very same rebel force at work in a sinner's external life is also at work in a rule-follower's inner life. Sin is not just an external action, it's an internal condition.

With spiritual sleight of hand and clever misdirection, the scribes and Pharisees of Jesus' day concealed their sins by pointing out the faults of others! Jesus loves rule-followers. However, His compassion to them sounds like an alarm and feels like urgency.

"**Woe** to you!…You hypocrites!" Jesus used the most explicit language He could to get their attention. "Woe" is a strong warning. It's as if Jesus was saying, "Stop! The bridge is out! The path you're on leads to destruction and you can't even see it!"

What are the key indicators of the path Jesus points out? "You clean the outside of the cup and dish, but inside you are full of greed and self-indulgence." Rule-followers can become obsessed with outward appearance. Jesus lovingly shines a bright light on their insidious enemy. Sin is an internal condition. Jesus is saying, "Oh rule-keeper, don't you see?! The rebel force you oppose is resident in your own heart."

Are you a rule-following scribe/Pharisee? Or are you a rebel tax collector/sinner? Jesus loves you right where you are. But He loves you too much to leave you where you are.

NOTHING LIKE JESUS

"You blind Pharisee! First clean the inside of the cup and the plate, that the outside also may be clean."
MATTHEW 23:26 ESV

From a religious and socio-political perspective, no one seemed to be more like Jesus than the scribes and Pharisees. He was, after all, a Jewish rabbi who had faithfully kept the law since He was a boy. He taught in their synagogues and paid their temple taxes. He dressed like them, ate like them, followed their customs, celebrated their feasts, and honored their Sabbath. Yet, Jesus couldn't have been more different than the scribes and Pharisees.

He often confronted their use of power and their understanding of the laws of Moses. He confounded their wisest teachers and frustrated their most powerful leaders. His agenda was completely cross-grained to theirs.

"You blind Pharisee!" Jesus pleaded with them to see. Why couldn't they? The very people who were most like Jesus couldn't see Him for who He really was. The Messiah they prayed for was right in front of them. But it's not just that they wouldn't admit it. They couldn't see it. In 1 John 1:8, John explains it this way:

"If we say we have no sin, we deceive ourselves, and the truth is not in us."

The scribes and Pharisees missed Jesus because they refused to deal with the condition of their hearts. They deceived themselves. Jesus offered them a way out. "First clean the inside…" As if to say, "Let's talk about your internal condition."

Most of us believe we're basically good people. Or at least we believe we're not as bad as "those people" (whoever they may be). Sure we mess up every once in a while, but we have the best of intentions and somehow that makes us good. But what if this is the very assumption that is causing us to miss our Savior?

Don't miss Him. He's not in a battle for your good behavior. There's something deeper He's after. He wants you to see your sin for what it is. It's a fatal condition that only He can heal. Let the concept of sin as a condition take you to the end of yourself. Humble yourself before Him and He will lift you up (James 4:10).

NOTES

BIBLE READING & MEDITATION

Grab a real paper Bible so that you can write in the margins, highlight verses, and make it your own. Read the following passages, meditate what you've read, and jot down your personal reflections.

DAY ONE

READ.

This is the evil in everything that happens under the sun: The same destiny overtakes all. The hearts of people, moreover, are full of evil and there is madness in their hearts while they live, and afterward they join the dead.

ECCLESIASTES 9:3 NIV

If we say we have no sin, we deceive ourselves, and the truth is not in us. If we confess our sins, He is faithful and just to forgive us our sins and to cleanse us from all unrighteousness.

1 JOHN 1:8-9 ESV

REFLECT.

- What does this tell me about God?

- What does this tell me about myself?

- How would this change my life if I took it seriously?

WRITE.

DAY TWO

READ.

Behold, I was brought forth in iniquity, and in sin did my mother conceive me. Behold, You delight in truth in the inward being, and You teach me wisdom in the secret heart.

PSALM 51:5-6 ESV

For all have sinned and fall short of the glory of God, and are justified by His grace as a gift, through the redemption that is in Christ Jesus...

ROMANS 3:23-24 ESV

REFLECT.

- What does this tell me about God?

- What does this tell me about myself?

- How would this change my life if I took it seriously?

WRITE.

DAY THREE

READ.

See to it, brothers and sisters, that none of you has a sinful, unbelieving heart that turns away from the living God. But encourage one another daily, as long as it is called 'Today,' so that none of you may be hardened by sin's deceitfulness.

HEBREWS 3:12-13 NIV

Therefore, confess your sins to one another and pray for one another, that you may be healed. The prayer of a righteous person has great power as it is working.

JAMES 5:16 ESV

REFLECT.

- What does this tell me about God?

- What does this tell me about myself?

- How would this change my life if I took it seriously?

WRITE.

DAY FOUR

READ.

Very rarely will anyone die for a righteous person, though for a good person someone might possibly dare to die. But God demonstrates His own love for us in this: While we were still sinners, Christ died for us.

ROMANS 5:7-8 NIV

The saying is trustworthy and deserving of full acceptance, that Christ Jesus came into the world to save sinners, of whom I am the foremost.

1 TIMOTHY 1:15 ESV

REFLECT.

- What does this tell me about God?

- What does this tell me about myself?

- How would this change my life if I took it seriously?

WRITE.

DAY FIVE

READ.

"If you love Me, you will keep My commandments."
JOHN 14:15 ESV

I pray that out of His glorious riches He may strengthen you with power through His Spirit in your inner being, so that Christ may dwell in your hearts through faith. And I pray that you, being rooted and established in love, may have power, together with all the Lord's holy people, to grasp how wide and long and high and deep is the love of Christ, and to know this love that surpasses knowledge.
EPHESIANS 3:16-19A NIV

REFLECT.

- What does this tell me about God?
- What does this tell me about myself?
- How would this change my life if I took it seriously?

WRITE.

GROUP TIME

OPENING THOUGHTS

After a time of introductions or catching up, open with prayer and give everyone an opportunity to share their thoughts on this week's topic.

Use The Big Idea and Starter Questions to open discussion and encourage people to reflect on their Pre-Group study. Ask about personal observations, pressing questions, or unique insights from this week's study.

GROWING CONNECTED

THE BIG IDEA

Sin is not just an external action, it's an internal condition.

STARTER QUESTIONS

1. What is your earliest memory of committing a sin? How did you know it was a sin? Did you get caught or did your conscience bother you? Explain.

2. Is there something you didn't realize was considered a sin until you were an adult?

3. When it comes to other people's sins, do you lean more toward mercy or justice?

VIDEO TEACHING

Write down any thoughts or ideas that stand out to you from
this week's teaching.

DISCUSSION QUESTIONS

1. Do you identify more with the "sinners and tax collectors" or the "scribes and Pharisees"? And why?

2. What are examples you've seen of how hidden sin will eventually hurt people?

3. Do you have someone in your life who knows your story, struggle, and secrets? If so, do you mind sharing what that relationship is like?

GROUP PRAYER TIME

Open up the floor for prayer requests. Pray for your group as a whole and for any individual requests.

GROUP PRAYER REQUESTS

pharisees- rule followers

NEXT STEPS

Author Rosaria Butterfield said, "One very difficult aspect about sin is that my sin never feels like sin to me. My sin feels like life, plain and simple." The internal motivations for sin are that way. They're hard to see in the mirror and when we do, they're easy to justify. But if you slow down long enough and get really honest with God, He'll show you the truth. And it's only the truth you know that leads to freedom.

Your personal challenge this week is called "Can I Be Honest?" This one's going to be fun and, fair warning, it may sting a little bit, too. Consider this exercise a conversation between you and God. Write out how you honestly feel about two or three specific sins you struggle with and ask God to help you see the truth. Use the list of questions below to guide you through.

- Who do I blame for my anger issues?

- Why do I like to gossip?

- Who am I envious of right now?

- Why don't I take care of my body? **OR** Why do I obsess over my body?

- Why do I justify my lust? Why do I fantasize about people I shouldn't?

- Why do I think I'm better than people?

- Who would I enjoy seeing fail? Why?

- What might I be addicted to? Why?

- Am I lazy? **OR** Why do I overwork?

- Am I greedy?

- Who or what am I coveting?

- Why don't I really honor the Sabbath?

- Why do I cheat, lie, or steal in tiny, unnoticeable ways?

NEXT STEPS EXERCISE

God, I admit I *might be addicted to my phone in general and maybe Instagram in specific.*

But, can I be honest? It's because *I want to be. I just honestly like the way it makes me feel. Sometimes I open my phone to do something productive and I get distracted. I forget why I'm there and I find myself mindlessly scrolling through my Instagram feed or watching videos. Part of me feels like I just wasted an hour of my day but the other part of me doesn't really see what's wrong with it. It's hard to tell when this crosses over from harmless entertainment to being sinful. I know I should find my comfort in You, but how does that really work? And how does this addiction (if You want to call it that) hurt my relationship with You?*

Help me see this the way You see it. I want to do better, so I give this to You. Please forgive me and help me love You more in this area. In Jesus' name, amen.

NEXT STEPS EXERCISE
CAN I BE HONEST?

God, I admit I

But, can I be honest? It's because

Help me see this the way You see it. I want to do better, so I give
this sin to You. Please forgive me and help me love You more in
this area. In Jesus' name, amen.

CAN I BE HONEST?

God, I admit I

But, can I be honest? It's because

Help me see this the way You see it. I want to do better, so I give this sin to You. Please forgive me and help me love You more in this area. In Jesus' name, amen.

CAN I BE HONEST?

God, I admit I

....

....

....

....

But, can I be honest? It's because

....

....

....

....

....

....

....

....

....

....

....

....

Help me see this the way You see it. I want to do better, so I give
this sin to You. Please forgive me and help me love You more in
this area. In Jesus' name, amen.

SESSION FOUR

REAL FORGIVENESS

PRE-GROUP

THE BIG IDEA
Real forgiveness always leads to real love.

HOW MUCH DO I OWE?
"A certain moneylender had two debtors. One owed five hundred denarii, and the other fifty. When they could not pay, he cancelled the debt of both. Now which of them will love him more?" Simon answered, "The one, I suppose, for whom he cancelled the larger debt." And He said to him, "You have judged rightly."

LUKE 7:41-43 ESV

Can you imagine what it must have been like to meet the *real* Jesus? Luke chapter 7 shares the story of a Pharisee named Simon who not only met Jesus, but also invited Him over for dinner. Maybe to his surprise, Jesus accepted. And in a moment's time, the sin-forgiving, miracle-working, all-wise rabbi was right there in front of Simon spending an evening in his home. Simon should have been euphoric at this honor. Yet somehow this rule-keeping Pharisee seemed to be indifferent.

Enter "a woman of the city." News had spread that Jesus was at Simon's house and this woman wasted no time in getting there. She could hardly wait to see Jesus. She made her way into the house and there He was. She was immediately overcome with emotion. Dinner conversation may have continued among the guests, but from that moment on, all eyes were on her.

What happened next must have been an intense thing to witness. She got down on her knees and began to wash Jesus' feet, not with water from a basin, but with the very tears that streamed down her face. She wiped His feet with her hair. Then she profusely kissed His feet and lavishly covered them with expensive oil. She had seized her opportunity to show earnest, heartfelt gratitude to her Messiah for the forgiveness He offered.

Look at the contrast! Simon the rule-follower didn't even provide Jesus with a customary foot-washing from one of his servants. This woman (the sinner) gave Jesus a foot-washing fit for a king with her own hands. The rule-follower judged Jesus for His bleeding-heart compassion. The sinner poured out her heart to Jesus for not judging her in her many sins. The rule-follower was aloof. The sinner was deeply moved to tears.

Have you experienced forgiveness of your sins? How much did your forgiveness cost God? Maybe you're a pretty good person. You'd never say it, but in your heart of hearts do you think it cost Jesus less to forgive you than it did for Him to forgive other people? I mean look at them. They chose to make a mess of their lives. You chose better. How much do you really owe God for your sin? Did Jesus really have to die for you? Isn't that a bit much?

The degree to which you understand what your forgiveness cost is the degree to which you understand the Gospel.

HOW MUCH DO I LOVE?

Then turning toward the woman He said to Simon, "Do you see this woman? I entered your house; you gave Me no water for My feet, but she has wet My feet with her tears and wiped them with her hair. You gave Me no kiss, but from the time I came in she has not ceased to kiss My feet. You did not anoint My head with oil, but she has anointed My feet with ointment. Therefore I tell you, her sins, which are many, are forgiven—for she loved much. But he who is forgiven little, loves little." And He said to her, "Your sins are forgiven."

LUKE 7:44-48 ESV

Love is the chief indicator of someone who knows what their forgiveness cost. Simon the Pharisee saw himself as having achieved goodness by his own merit. He earned his righteousness by making right choices. "But he who is forgiven little, loves little." Simon's own goodness blinded him to the truth about his sin. It was impossible for him to love sinners and it was impossible for him to love Jesus. His heart had been hardened by pride.

The woman, on the other hand, couldn't help herself from loving. Jesus said, "She loved much…" She loved much because she realized how much she had been loved. God had so loved her that He sent Jesus to her. In spite of the debt of her sin, Jesus loved her. In spite of what it cost Him to forgive her, He offered it freely. How could she not show love in return?

Do you love much? Are you moved with compassion for people who are far from God? Are you, from time to time, overcome with emotion when you think of what Jesus did for you? Is the thought of what your forgiveness cost sometimes too much to bear?

You cannot change a problem you're not willing to admit exists. When you acknowledge the truth about your sin, real forgiveness is possible. Only then can you start to understand how to love. Real forgiveness always leads to real love.

NOTES

NOTES

BIBLE READING & MEDITATION

Grab a real paper Bible so that you can write in the margins, highlight verses, and make it your own. Read the following passages, meditate what you've read, and jot down your personal reflections.

DAY ONE

READ.

So where does that put us? Do we Jews get a better break than the others? Not really. Basically, all of us, whether insiders or outsiders, start out in identical conditions, which is to say that we all start out as sinners. Scripture leaves no doubt about it:

There's nobody living right, not even one, nobody who knows the score, nobody alert for God. They've all taken the wrong turn; they've all wandered down blind alleys. No one's living right; I can't find a single one."

ROMANS 3:9-12 MSG

REFLECT.

- What does this tell me about God?

- What does this tell me about myself?

- How would this change my life if I took it seriously?

WRITE.

DAY TWO

READ.

Behold what manner of love the Father has bestowed on us, that we should be called children of God! Therefore the world does not know us, because it did not know Him.

1 JOHN 3:1 NKJV

This is love: not that we loved God, but that He loved us and sent His Son as an atoning sacrifice for our sins.

1 JOHN 4:10 NIV

REFLECT.

- What does this tell me about God?

- What does this tell me about myself?

- How would this change my life if I took it seriously?

WRITE.

DAY THREE

READ.

"Therefore I tell you, her sins, which are many, are forgiven—for she loved much. But he who is forgiven little, loves little."
LUKE 7:47 ESV

But God, being rich in mercy, because of the great love with which He loved us, even when we were dead in our trespasses, made us alive together with Christ—by grace you have been saved.
EPHESIANS 2:4-5 ESV

REFLECT.

- What does this tell me about God?

- What does this tell me about myself?

- How would this change my life if I took it seriously?

WRITE.

DAY FOUR

READ.

Jesus said, "Father, forgive them, for they do not know what they are doing."

LUKE 23:34 NIV

"For I will forgive their wickedness and will remember their sins no more."

HEBREWS 8:12 NIV

REFLECT.

- What does this tell me about God?

- What does this tell me about myself?

- How would this change my life if I took it seriously?

WRITE.

DAY FIVE

READ.

*"I, even I, am He who blots out your transgressions for My
own sake; And I will not remember your sins. Put Me in
remembrance; Let us contend together; State your case,
that you may be acquitted."*
ISAIAH 43:25-26 NKJV

*You know you were not bought and made free from sin by paying
gold or silver which comes to an end. And you know you were
not saved from the punishment of sin by the way of life that you
were given from your early fathers. That way of life was worth
nothing. The blood of Christ saved you. This blood is of great
worth and no amount of money can buy it. Christ was given
as a lamb without sin and without spot.*
1 PETER 1:18-19 NLV

REFLECT.

- What does this tell me about God?
- What does this tell me about myself?
- How would this change my life if I took it seriously?

WRITE.

GROUP TIME

OPENING THOUGHTS

After a time of introductions or catching up, open with prayer and give everyone an opportunity to share their thoughts on this week's topic.

Use The Big Idea and Starter Questions to open discussion and encourage people to reflect on their Pre-Group study. Ask about personal observations, pressing questions, or unique insights from this week's study.

GROWING CONNECTED

THE BIG IDEA

Real forgiveness always leads to real love.

STARTER QUESTIONS

1. Was the family culture you grew up in quick to forgive or quick to hold grudges?

2. Have you ever destroyed or damaged something expensive and had to ask for forgiveness from the owner? Tell us about it.

3. Have you ever had someone pay a large debt on your behalf? Tell us about it.

VIDEO TEACHING

Write down any thoughts or ideas that stand out to you from this week's teaching.

DISCUSSION QUESTIONS

1. If Jesus showed up to your house for dinner,
    how would you react?

2. When is the last time you were overcome with emotion in
    a church service or a personal prayer time? Tell us about it.

3. What barriers get in the way of admitting you're a sinner?

4. What would the people closest to you say about your
    love for Jesus?

5. If you had a meter that showed your compassion for
    people far from God, what would it read?

GROUP PRAYER TIME

Open up the floor for prayer requests. Pray for your group
as a whole and for any individual requests.

GROUP PRAYER REQUESTS

NEXT STEPS

If you have not experienced the depth of real forgiveness from God, it may be that there's a significant obstacle in your way. Matthew 6:14 says, "For if you forgive other people when they sin against you, your heavenly Father will also forgive you." Big or small, practice forgiveness this week. It's one of the key ways you can experience the depth of God's love in your own life.

Your exercise this week is to write a Forgiveness Letter. Instructions and recommendations are on the next page. Use these questions to narrow down who you may want to address your letter to.

- Was there a bully, a sibling, or an older family member who hurt me in a way that impacted my life as a child?

- Did one of my parents, a teacher, a coach, or a leader say or do something that hurt me in a way that has stuck with me over the years?

- Was there a date, a girlfriend or boyfriend, or a spouse who hurt me?

- Was there a boss, a business partner, a pastor, or a trusted friend who hurt me?

- Is there someone I have hurt that I have yet to ask for forgiveness?

NEXT STEPS EXERCISE
FORGIVENESS LETTER INSTRUCTIONS

Consider this a first step toward forgiveness. Keep in mind that sending the letter you're about to write is not necessarily part of the exercise, though you may choose to do so. If you find yourself among those who are inclined to send it, be encouraged—you will notice a significant burden is lifted when you do.

Make this letter brief and use any medium you like to write it. Feel free to use the section provided on the next page of this book, or get some good old-fashioned pen and paper, or just use your favorite digital device.

Be as honest as you can about what happened. Identify the ways this has impacted your life over time. This was a big deal. It should not have happened. Let your words express the gravity of what they did, no more and no less. Be honest about the ways you may have contributed to them hurting you. Own anything you did that was wrong. Then offer forgiveness to them in light of what Jesus has done for you, e.g., "I can freely forgive you of any sins against me because I've found real forgiveness for my own sins in what Jesus has done for me."

Don't worry about grammar or spelling. Sometimes those things can be distractions to the real work of your heart. Additionally, should you decide to send your letter, it's best to sit on it for a day or two. Maybe let a trusted friend read it. Then re-read it yourself to ensure there's nothing that needs to be softened up, changed, or omitted.

Another Forgiveness Letter option is to write to someone from whom you need to ask forgiveness. In this case, you would follow the pattern above in reverse. Acknowledge what you did and that it should not have happened. Identify ways it may have impacted their life. Be honest about the ways they may have contributed to what you did, but fully own the consequences of your decision. Finally, ask for their forgiveness.

The point of the exercise is to allow the truth of the Gospel—the truth that you have been freely forgiven—to take hold of your heart. In a place where unforgiveness may currently reside, divine love is waiting to take up residence.

NEXT STEPS EXERCISE
FORGIVENESS LETTER

REAL GRACE

PRE-GROUP

THE BIG IDEA

The good news isn't really good until the bad news is really bad.

WHAT IS THE GOSPEL?

Jesus stood up and said to her, "Woman, where are they? Has no one condemned you?" She said, "No one, Lord." And Jesus said, "Neither do I condemn you; go, and from now on sin no more."
JOHN 8:10-11 ESV

The Gospel is not counsel or advice designed to make your life better. It's news. When someone gives you counsel you can take it or leave it. Its power to change you is dependent upon what you do with it. News is different. News is about something that has already happened. Its power to change you depends not on what you do, but on the nature of the news itself.

The Gospel of Jesus is not just news. Jesus claimed the Holy Spirit anointed Him "to proclaim good news…" (Luke 4:18). "Gospel" means "good news." But what's good about it? In a word, the good news of Jesus is "grace."

Through His death, burial, and resurrection Jesus made grace available to anyone who chooses Him (John 3:16). Justice is getting what you deserve. Mercy is not getting what you deserve. Grace transcends justice and mercy. Grace offers to give you what you don't deserve.

The woman caught in adultery in John chapter 8 knew her life was over. This was really bad news. She may have hoped for mercy, but she certainly expected justice. Her public execution was happening! How much worse could it get?

Rather than bludgeoning her to death immediately, the woman's accusers saw this as an opportunity to include Jesus in her judgment. Jesus, full of grace and truth, masterfully turned the bad news on the woman's accusers. "Let him who is without sin among you be the first to throw a stone at her..." (verse 7). One by one, her accusers walked away.

"Woman, where are they? Has no one condemned you?"
She said, "No one, Lord." [Jesus, gave her the good news of His grace.] *And Jesus said, "Neither do I condemn you; go, and from now on sin no more."*
JOHN 8:10-11 ESV

Consider this, though. If the scribes and Pharisees who walked away had stayed and confessed their sin to Jesus, what would He have said to them? Would He have judged them harshly and shamed them? Isn't that what they deserved? John 3:17 says, "God did not send His Son into the world to condemn the world, but that the world through Him might be saved."

Jesus' response to them would have been the same as His response to the woman. "Neither do I condemn you; go, and from now on sin no more." That's grace. That's the Gospel of Jesus.

But the good news isn't really good until the bad news is really bad. The bad news really is bad for you. Whether you're a rebel whose sin is evident to the world or you're an externally flawless, rule-keeping, law-abiding "scribe" or "Pharisee" whose sin is hidden from the world, you deserve the harshness of justice. We all do.

Mercy, if you could attain it, may get you back to square one. But even then your righteousness is not enough to attain Heaven. Only grace can save you. Only Jesus can save you. Only Jesus' grace will welcome us to Heaven.

Jesus was willing to be abandoned on that cross to not only rescue you from the truthful accusations of your sin, but to exchange His righteousness for yours.

"God made Him who had no sin to be sin for us, so that in Him we might become the righteousness of God."
2 CORINTHIANS 5:21 NIV

This is the good news. This is grace.

NOTES

NOTES

BIBLE READING & MEDITATION

Grab a real paper Bible so that you can write in the margins, highlight verses, and make it your own. Read the following passages, meditate what you've read, and jot down your personal reflections.

DAY ONE

READ.

Jesus stood up and said to her, "Woman, where are they? Has no one condemned you?" She said, "No one, Lord." And Jesus said, "Neither do I condemn you; go, and from now on sin no more."

JOHN 8:10-11 ESV

"He is so rich in kindness and grace that He purchased our freedom with the blood of His Son and forgave our sins. He has showered His kindness on us, along with all wisdom and understanding."

EPHESIANS 1:7-8 NLT

REFLECT.

- What does this tell me about God?

- What does this tell me about myself?

- How would this change my life if I took it seriously?

WRITE.

DAY TWO

READ.

And God saw that the wickedness of man was great in the earth, and that every imagination of the thoughts of his heart was only evil continually... But Noah found grace in the eyes of the Lord.

GENESIS 6:5, 8 KJV

The Word became a human being and, full of grace and truth, lived among us. We saw His glory, the glory which He received as the Father's only Son.

JOHN 1:14 GNT

REFLECT.

- What does this tell me about God?

- What does this tell me about myself?

- How would this change my life if I took it seriously?

WRITE.

DAY THREE

READ.

"Come now, and let us reason together, saith the Lord: though your sins be as scarlet, they shall be as white as snow; though they be red like crimson, they shall be as wool."

ISAIAH 1:18 KJV

And God is able to make all grace abound toward you, that you, always having all sufficiency in all things, may have an abundance for every good work.

2 CORINTHIANS 9:8 NKJV

REFLECT.

- What does this tell me about God?

- What does this tell me about myself?

- How would this change my life if I took it seriously?

WRITE.

DAY FOUR

READ.

For I am the least of the apostles and do not even deserve to be called an apostle, because I persecuted the church of God. But by the grace of God I am what I am, and His grace to me was not without effect. No, I worked harder than all of them—yet not I, but the grace of God that was with me."

1 CORINTHIANS 15:9-10 NIV

For it is by grace you have been saved, through faith—and this is not from yourselves, it is the gift of God—not by works, so that no one can boast.

EPHESIANS 2:8-9 NIV

REFLECT.

- What does this tell me about God?

- What does this tell me about myself?

- How would this change my life if I took it seriously?

WRITE.

DAY FIVE

READ.

For sin will have no dominion over you, since you are not under law but under grace.
ROMANS 6:14 ESV

Let us then approach God's throne of grace with confidence, so that we may receive mercy and find grace to help us in our time of need.
HEBREWS 4:16 NIV

REFLECT.

- What does this tell me about God?
- What does this tell me about myself?
- How would this change my life if I took it seriously?

WRITE.

GROUP TIME

OPENING THOUGHTS

After a time of introductions or catching up, open with prayer and give everyone an opportunity to share their thoughts on this week's topic.

Use The Big Idea and Starter Questions to open discussion and encourage people to reflect on their Pre-Group study. Ask about personal observations, pressing questions, or unique insights from this week's study.

GROWING CONNECTED

THE BIG IDEA

The good news isn't really good until the bad news is really bad.

STARTER QUESTIONS

1. Do you remember your first experience hearing the Gospel? Tell us about it.

2. Would you consider yourself more of a rule-keeper or a rebel? Explain.

3. Tell about a time you got caught doing something you weren't supposed to as a kid.

4. What misconceptions do you think people have about grace?

VIDEO TEACHING

Write down any thoughts or ideas that stand out to you from this week's teaching.

DISCUSSION QUESTIONS

1. The bad news is we're all far more sinful than we ever realized. If this is true, why do you think most people describe themselves as "a pretty good person"?

2. Grace says we're far more loved than we dared imagine. If this is true, why do you think so many people wrestle with low self-esteem or insecurity?

3. What meaningful moments of God's grace have you experienced in your life?

4. If you were to share your personal "good news" story in just two or three sentences, what would you say?

GROUP PRAYER TIME

Open up the floor for prayer requests. Pray for your group as a whole and for any individual requests.

GROUP PRAYER REQUESTS

NEXT STEPS

Put what you heard into practice this week by praying bold prayers. Ask God to show you hidden areas of your life you have yet to see in the light of His grace. Ask Him to help you surrender those areas to Jesus.

God has been gracious to you. You have people in your life that you love. Your exercise is very simple this week.

- Call someone you love.
- Let them know you've been thinking about God's grace on your life.
- Let them know why their name came to mind.
- Tell them why you love them.

That's it. When God's grace abounds toward you, you can't help but be grateful!

SESSION SIX

REAL SURRENDER

PRE-GROUP

THE BIG IDEA
There's always a cross before a resurrection.

FREEDOM IS HERE.
"The Son of Man must suffer many terrible things," He said.
"He will be rejected by the elders, the leading priests, and the
teachers of religious law. He will be killed, but on the third day
He will be raised from the dead."
LUKE 9:22 NLT

Jesus was surprisingly open about His death. He talked about it often, openly, and in great detail. Many prophets of old had foretold that Messiah would die and be raised back to life. Still, when Jesus pointed those predictions to Himself, it seemed to fall on deaf ears. His disciples just couldn't comprehend it (see Luke 18:34). They heard the words. They just didn't understand.

On this particular occasion, Peter had just declared that Jesus was the "Messiah sent from God!" What a radical claim.

To a first-century Jew, "Messiah" represented the culmination of hundreds of years of hopes, dreams, and desperate prayers. To a young man like Peter, "you are the Messiah" meant freedom had arrived! Freedom from the tyranny of Rome, freedom to worship God as His chosen people, and freedom to prosper once again in the land God had promised their forefathers.

Freedom is a notion we can all get behind. We all want a Messiah who can free us. What kind of freedom are you pursuing in your life? Freedom in your finances? Freedom from an emotional wound? Freedom from fear, worry, stress, or anxiety? Freedom from hidden sin or an addiction? Freedom from loneliness or depression? When you start to talk to Jesus about freedom, He's going to start talking to you about death.

Consider how jarring it would have been for Peter to hear Jesus accept this astounding messianic endorsement in one sentence and immediately talk about His imminent defeat in the very next sentence! Jesus seemed to be contradicting Himself. This is a non sequitur—the logic doesn't follow. "I'm your ticket to freedom. I'm about to die…" makes no sense.

We have such a strong aversion to death, don't we? We're repulsed by it. We don't like it at all. But notice Jesus didn't only talk about death. He talked about death and resurrection. The disciples couldn't understand the resurrection part of what Jesus said, because they couldn't get past the death part of what He said. They knew what we all know. Death is inevitable and resurrection is impossible.

But Jesus was talking about freedom, because in Him resurrection is possible. And death always comes before freedom, because there's always a cross before a resurrection.

SURRENDER IS NECESSARY.

Then He said to the crowd, "If any of you wants to be My follower, you must give up your own way, take up your cross daily, and follow Me."
LUKE 9:23 NLT

When you read the words "take up your cross" what image comes to mind? If you grew up in church or have read through the Gospels, you may color these words with thoughts of the man who helped Jesus carry His cross up to the hill where He was crucified. But this couldn't have been the image Jesus was evoking because it hadn't happened yet.

The crucifixion of Jesus was neither the first nor the last cross the disciples would have seen. The cross was Rome's favorite tool for torture and public execution. The disciples had seen it countless times. Disreputable criminals and revolting rebels were often paraded through the streets of Jerusalem carrying the very crosses on which they would be hung to die. "Surrender!" was the message of the Roman cross. It was inhumane, grotesque, and despicable. To a devout Jew, the cross symbolized the very ideals they desperately hoped their Messiah would defeat. And Jesus had the gall to say, "take up your cross daily, and follow Me"? What a terribly haunting thing to say!

Jesus was using the most evocative language available to tell His followers that surrender is necessary. He had often used the reality of Roman oppression to teach a new, transcendent way to look at surrender. "If an evil person slaps you on your right cheek, turn the other to him also…" and "If anyone forces you to go with them one mile, go with them two." (Matthew 5:39, 41).

Forced surrender is not true surrender. True surrender is loosening your grip on the here and now, letting go of your earthly rights, and seeing your life in light of eternity. No image better represented the cares of this world than the cross. And Jesus compels His followers to take it up daily. Not just because it leads you to the end of yourself, but because it leads you to the beginning of resurrected life in Him.

No matter what it costs you, take up your cross today. Surrender is necessary because resurrection life is the only life worth living.

NOTES

NOTES

BIBLE READING & MEDITATION

Grab a real paper Bible so that you can write in the margins, highlight verses, and make it your own. Read the following passages, meditate what you've read, and jot down your personal reflections.

DAY ONE

READ.

Then He [Jesus] said to them, "My soul is overwhelmed with sorrow to the point of death. Stay here and keep watch with Me." Going a little farther, He fell with His face to the ground and prayed, "My Father, if it is possible, may this cup be taken from Me. Yet not as I will, but as You will."

MATTHEW 26:38-39 NIV

The angel said to the women, "Do not be afraid, for I know that you are looking for Jesus, who was crucified. He is not here; He has risen, just as He said. Come and see the place where He lay."

MATTHEW 28:5-6 NIV

REFLECT.

- What does this tell me about God?

- What does this tell me about myself?

- How would this change my life if I took it seriously?

WRITE.

DAY TWO

READ.

Jesus said to her, "Your brother will rise again." Martha said to Him, "I know that He will rise again in the resurrection at the last day."

Jesus said to her, "I am the resurrection and the life. He who believes in Me, though he may die, he shall live. And whoever lives and believes in Me shall never die. Do you believe this?"

JOHN 11:24-26 NKJV

If you declare with your mouth, "Jesus is Lord," and believe in your heart that God raised Him from the dead, you will be saved.

ROMANS 10:9 NIV

REFLECT.

- What does this tell me about God?

- What does this tell me about myself?

- How would this change my life if I took it seriously?

WRITE.

DAY THREE

READ.

For we know that our old self was crucified with Him so that the body ruled by sin might be done away with, that we should no longer be slaves to sin…

ROMANS 6:6 NIV

I have been crucified with Christ and I no longer live, but Christ lives in me. The life I now live in the body, I live by faith in the Son of God, who loved me and gave Himself for me.

GALATIANS 2:20 NIV

REFLECT.

- What does this tell me about God?

- What does this tell me about myself?

- How would this change my life if I took it seriously?

WRITE.

DAY FOUR

READ.

It was for this freedom that Christ set us free [completely liberating us].

GALATIANS 5:1 AMP

So if the Son makes you free, then you are unquestionably free.

JOHN 8:36 AMP

REFLECT.

- What does this tell me about God?
- What does this tell me about myself?
- How would this change my life if I took it seriously?

WRITE.

DAY FIVE

READ.

Let not sin therefore reign in your mortal body, to make you obey its passions. Do not present your members to sin as instruments for unrighteousness, but present yourselves to God as those who have been brought from death to life, and your members to God as instruments for righteousness.

ROMANS 6:12-13 ESV

By faith Moses, when he had grown up, refused to be known as the son of Pharaoh's daughter. He chose to be mistreated along with the people of God rather than to enjoy the fleeting pleasures of sin. He regarded disgrace for the sake of Christ as of greater value than the treasures of Egypt, because he was looking ahead to his reward.

HEBREWS 11:24-26 NIV

REFLECT.

- What does this tell me about God?
- What does this tell me about myself?
- How would this change my life if I took it seriously?

WRITE.

GROUP TIME

OPENING THOUGHTS

After a time of introductions or catching up, open with prayer and give everyone an opportunity to share their thoughts on this week's topic.

Use The Big Idea and Starter Questions to open discussion and encourage people to reflect on their Pre-Group study. Ask about personal observations, pressing questions, or unique insights from this week's study.

GROWING CONNECTED

THE BIG IDEA

There's always a cross before a resurrection.

STARTER QUESTIONS

1. Today, crosses are everywhere. You see them on church steeples, on headstones, and on Christian t-shirts. They're used as landmarks, as jewelry, and even tattoos. What do you think the symbol of the cross meant to a first-century Jew?

2. What did the cross mean to Jesus?

3. What does the symbol of the cross mean to you?

VIDEO TEACHING

Write down any thoughts or ideas that stand out to you from this week's teaching.

Nov. 19 & 20 - Real Jesus
weekend

DISCUSSION QUESTIONS

1. What kind of freedom does your Real Jesus journey represent to you?

2. What makes surrender so difficult for people in general and you personally?

3. What does it mean to you personally to take up your cross daily and follow Jesus? What specific situation in your life requires this of you right now?

4. Who is someone in your life who knows your story, struggle, and secrets?

GROUP PRAYER TIME

Open up the floor for prayer requests. Pray for your group as a whole and for any individual requests.

GROUP PRAYER REQUESTS

NEXT STEPS

Your exercise this week is called "A Declaration of Surrender." Your assignment is to set up an appointment with someone in this group with whom you can share your story, struggle, and secrets. Then, you can hear their story as well. These conversations are confidential. This is a brave space. Freedom lies on the other side.

Use these questions to unearth things you might share when you meet. Be prepared to follow through with wise next steps. When you meet with one another, remember to listen well and extend grace to one another.

- What sins did I inherit from previous generations that give me the most trouble?

- If I were to make a total wreck of my life, what sin would most likely be the cause?

- Is there something that happened a long time ago that I've never told anyone?

- What's a problem I've resolved to fix myself but wouldn't dare ask for help?

- Is there something I'm doing right now that I'd be ashamed if people knew?

- What could freedom look like on the other side of surrender?

NEXT STEPS EXERCISE
A DECLARATION OF SURRENDER

The Name of Your Group Partner:

Time of Your Call, Text, or Email:

Date / Time of Your Appointment:

Notes to Yourself After Your Conversation:

REAL RESURRECTION

PRE-GROUP

THE BIG IDEA

We often miss the greatest things because our hopes are set on lesser things.

YOUR GOD IS TOO SMALL

"About Jesus of Nazareth," they replied. "He was a prophet, powerful in word and deed before God and all the people. The chief priests and our rulers handed Him over to be sentenced to death, and they crucified Him."

LUKE 24:19-20 NIV

Who is Jesus, really? You say He's God, but has that affected your daily life? Are you living as if your Savior and friend is also the King of all Kings and Lord of all Lords? Or is your view of God too small?

Consider Peter, who Jesus praised for recognizing that He was indeed "…the Messiah, the son of the living God." Yet a moment later Jesus rebuked Peter, saying "For you are not setting your mind on the things of God, but on the things of man," (see Matthew 16:13-23). As if to say, "Peter, you acknowledge that I'm God, but your God is too small."

Consider John the Baptist, of whom Jesus said, "no one among those born of woman is greater..." (see Luke 7). Yet even John the Baptist began to question who Jesus really was, asking, "Are you the one who is to come, or should we expect someone else?" Jesus had just raised someone from the dead—the son of a widow in the village of Nain—before John's doubts reached Jesus' ears.

Consider the people of Nain in the aftermath of this young boy's resurrection. "Fear seized them all..." and they said, "A great prophet has arisen," (Luke 7:16). While this seems like the right thing to say, "prophet" was a woefully inadequate description of who Jesus really was.

Consider the disciples on the road to Emmaus from Luke 24. Jesus hid His identity from them in order to draw out their honest answers to this critical question: Who is Jesus, really? Look at their descriptions. "Jesus of Nazareth"—accurate. "Prophet"—true. "Powerful in word and deed"—that's correct. Yet, just like the people of Nain, and like John the Baptist, and like Peter, their view of Jesus was too small. The highest praise they could muster showed just how restrained their expectations were. He was right in front of them, yet they missed who He really was!

If the people closest to Jesus—the ones who watched Him raise the dead, walk on water, cast out demons, feed the five thousand, heal the sick, calm the storm, and confound the scribes and Pharisees—if these people had a limited view of who Jesus really was, what about you and me? How could our frame of reference not be limited? How could our expectations not be restrained?

1 Corinthians 13:12 expresses it this way…

*"For now we see in a mirror dimly, but then face to face.
Now I know in part; then I shall know fully, even as I have
been fully known."*

Who is Jesus to you, really? He's greater than you think He is.

YOUR HOPES ARE TOO SMALL

*"…but we had hoped that He was the one who was going
to redeem Israel."*

LUKE 24:21 ESV

We miss the greatest things because our hopes are set on lesser things. Isn't this true? If our view of God is too small, our hopes are too small as well.

The Emmaus Road disciples were leaving Jerusalem. The miracles of Jesus were over. The fanfare was over. The movement was over. It was time to pack up and go home. As they spoke with their new traveling companion, the veiled Son of God, they mourned the death of hope itself.

Surely this was not what God had in mind for the people of Israel! Roman oppression left to continue unchallenged? Herod left to evangelize Israel with his pagan, Hellenistic philosophies? "We had hoped, dear sojourner, that this prophet, Jesus, mighty in word and deed, would redeem Israel…"

They had a sophisticated perspective on the complex nature of the problems of their day. Culture wars. Political upheaval. Social issues. Religious divisions among God's own people. Their view of Messiah was as nuanced and thoughtful as their view of the world. Yet their hopes were too small.

Resurrection life Himself was walking beside them! Their focus on external problems caused them to miss what Jesus was really after—their heart! "How foolish you are, and how slow to believe all that the prophets have spoken!" Jesus said.

They missed eternal joy because their hopes were set on external problems. Jesus opened the scriptures and revealed Himself to them as their resurrected Savior, and at once they caught a glimpse of His eternal perspective, "Were not our hearts burning within us?"

How easy it is for us to do the same! External pressures and instant pleasures surround us every day, vying for our money, our attention, and our affection. Have we set our hopes on external problems when what Jesus offers is eternal joy? Do we really believe resurrection is possible in every area of life?

Jesus opened their eyes to His mission—death to death itself and resurrection life to all who believe! Jesus was not after a political revolution, an economic revival, or even social justice. Jesus was after an eternal reward—joy in the hearts of His people.

NOTES

BIBLE READING & MEDITATION

Grab a real paper Bible so that you can write in the margins, highlight verses, and make it your own. Read the following passages, meditate what you've read, and jot down your personal reflections.

DAY ONE

READ.

*And being found in human form, He humbled himself
by becoming obedient to the point of death, even death on a
cross. Therefore God has highly exalted Him and bestowed on
Him the name that is above every name, so that at the name of
Jesus every knee should bow, in heaven and on earth and under
the earth, and every tongue confess that Jesus Christ is Lord, to the
glory of God the Father.*

PHILIPPIANS 2:8-11 ESV

*Then He said to Thomas, "Put your finger into My hands. Put your
hand into My side. Don't be faithless any longer. Believe!" "My
Lord and my God!" Thomas said. Then Jesus told him, 'You believe
because you have seen Me. But blessed are those who haven't seen
Me and believe anyway."*

JOHN 20:27-29 TLB

REFLECT.

- What does this tell me about God?

- What does this tell me about myself?

- How would this change my life if I took it seriously?

WRITE.

DAY TWO

READ.

When I saw Him, I fell at His feet as though dead. Then He placed His right hand on me and said: "Do not be afraid. I am the First and the Last. I am the Living One; I was dead, and now look, I am alive for ever and ever!"

REVELATION 1:17-18 NIV

Surrender your heart to God, turn to Him in prayer, and give up your sins—even those you do in secret. Then you won't be ashamed; you will be confident and fearless.

JOB 11:13-15 CEV

REFLECT.

- What does this tell me about God?

- What does this tell me about myself?

- How would this change my life if I took it seriously?

WRITE.

DAY THREE

READ.

But if there is no resurrection of the dead, then not even Christ has been raised. And if Christ has not been raised, then our preaching is in vain and your faith is in vain.

1 CORINTHIANS 15:13-14 ESV

But God raised Him from the dead, releasing Him from the agony of death, because it was impossible for Him to be held in its clutches.

ACTS 2:24 BEREAN STUDY BIBLE

REFLECT.

- What does this tell me about God?

- What does this tell me about myself?

- How would this change my life if I took it seriously?

WRITE.

DAY FOUR

READ.

Therefore, since we are surrounded by so great a cloud of witnesses, let us also lay aside every weight, and sin which clings so closely, and let us run with endurance the race that is set before us, looking to Jesus, the founder and perfecter of our faith, who for the joy that was set before Him endured the cross, despising the shame, and is seated at the right hand of the throne of God.

HEBREWS 12:1-3 ESV

If then you have been raised with Christ, seek the things that are above, where Christ is, seated at the right hand of God. Set your minds on things that are above, not on things that are on earth. For you have died, and your life is hidden with Christ in God. When Christ who is your life appears, then you also will appear with Him in glory.

COLOSSIANS 3:1-4 ESV

REFLECT.

- What does this tell me about God?

- What does this tell me about myself?

- How would this change my life if I took it seriously?

WRITE.

DAY FIVE

READ.

Then shall come to pass the saying that is written:
"Death is swallowed up in victory."
"O death, where is your victory?
O death, where is your sting?"

1 CORINTHIANS 15:54B-55 ESV

I appeal to you therefore, brothers, by the mercies of God,
to present your bodies as a living sacrifice, holy and acceptable
to God, which is your spiritual worship. Do not be conformed to
this world, but be transformed by the renewal of your mind, that
by testing you may discern what is the will of God, what is good
and acceptable and perfect.

ROMANS 12:1-2 ESV

REFLECT.

- What does this tell me about God?
- What does this tell me about myself?
- How would this change my life if I took it seriously?

WRITE.

GROUP TIME

OPENING THOUGHTS

After a time of introductions or catching up, open with prayer and give everyone an opportunity to share their thoughts on this week's topic.

Use The Big Idea and Starter Questions to open discussion and encourage people to reflect on their Pre-Group study. Ask about personal observations, pressing questions, or unique insights from this week's study.

GROWING CONNECTED

THE BIG IDEA

We often miss the greatest things because our hopes are set on lesser things.

STARTER QUESTIONS

1. If you could ask God to fix one thing in our world right now, what would it be?

2. If you could ask God to fix one thing in your family right now, what would it be?

3. Do you ever feel like God doesn't understand your hopes? What makes you feel this way?

4. What have you learned about the *real* Jesus that you wish the world could know?

VIDEO TEACHING

Write down any thoughts or ideas that stand out to you from this week's teaching.

DISCUSSION QUESTIONS

1. What's one of your greatest personal disappointments?

2. What's one of your greatest personal hopes?

3. What problems or pleasures are most likely to distract you from God's best for your life?

4. Last week's Next Steps assignment was "A Declaration of Surrender." Some of you took a step to share your story, struggle, and secrets with a friend. How did it go?

GROUP PRAYER TIME

Open up the floor for prayer requests. Pray for your group as a whole and for any individual requests.

PRAYER REQUESTS

NEXT STEPS

Last week we talked about surrender. That there's always a cross before a resurrection. You made a commitment to surrender your sin to Jesus. Have you surrendered your hopes as well? Do you believe resurrection is possible? The Emmaus Road disciples thought Jesus had let them down. Their sincere hopes had turned to desperate disappointments. Jesus showed them something greater than their hopes. He wants to do the same for you.

Your exercise this week is to create a "Hopes and Hang-ups List." Think back to the hopes and disappointments that may have shaped you. Take advantage of these questions to bring specific moments to light.

- What kind of ideal life and family have I hoped for?

- What does financial security look like in my hopes and dreams?

- When did God not come through for me in the way I thought He should?

- How has a church or a Christian friend let me down?

- How have I let myself down?

- How can Jesus satisfy my greatest hopes and heal my deepest disappointments?

HOPES & HANG-UPS

- Terry & Linda's son
- protection - Alex
-
- Dana Sue - guidance (God)
- place in life
-
- Jay - "
-
- Elise -
-
- Justin - understanding of
- place in life
-
-
-
-
-

REAL POWER

PRE-GROUP

In the week leading up to Group Time, set aside about 45 minutes to work through these Pre-Group resources. You'll not only get know Jesus better, but your insights and personal reflections will make your Group Time better as well.

THE BIG IDEA

Jesus gives you the power to be a witness.

A NEW KIND OF POWER.

"But you will receive power when the Holy Spirit comes on you; and you will be My witnesses in Jerusalem, and in all Judea and Samaria, and to the ends of the earth."

ACTS 1:8 NIV

What is a witness?

In recent years, public opinion polls have shown that many Americans now believe that Christians who share their faith are considered "extremist." Even among professing Christians, there is much debate about the ways we should or should not present our beliefs to the world. Here are two basic views.

Some consider evangelism as a kind of moral duty. "We're right. You're wrong. Come to the right side." Certainly this is offensive. On the other side of the spectrum would be the relativist view. "It's not our place to judge anyone." Different as they may be, neither of these views have much power to impact the world.

Jesus clearly told His disciples, "You will receive power... to be My witnesses." So what did He mean? How was it supposed to work? And what kind of power was He connecting to this ideal?

As you read through the narrative of Acts chapters 1 and 2, you'll notice that the disciples started out with one view of power and they ended up completely transformed by a different view of power. And they couldn't stop talking about it. What happened?

The resurrected Jesus had appeared to them for 40 days. He hung out with them, shared a few meals, and kept talking about this new kind of power. The disciples did their best to understand what He meant.

So when (the disciples) had come together, they asked Him,
"Lord, will You at this time restore the kingdom to Israel?"
ACTS 1:6 ESV

"Kingdom" was the major theme of Jesus' ministry. But whenever He said "kingdom of God," the disciples heard "kingdom of Israel." Who can blame them, though? Many of them were zealous Israeli nationalists when He recruited them. The only power they had ever known was political, military, cultural, and religious power. What else could Jesus mean by "kingdom"? Of course He was planning to overthrow the evil empire!

To their great surprise, Jesus didn't start a political revolution. Instead, He shot up in the sky and ascended into Heaven right before their eyes. He left them standing there with their mouths open. Jesus is always up to something bigger than our expectations.

Jesus' last orders were to "stay in Jerusalem" and "wait for the promise of the Father." So they tucked their ambitious tails between their legs, waddled home, and waited.

We all come to Jesus with ambitions. We can't help it. But like the disciples, Jesus never shames us for it. He simply points us to something bigger. Before Jesus compels us to "go and tell" there's always a "stay and wait" involved. Why? Because He loves us.

Jesus uses the soft power of patience to loosen our grubby grip on our best-laid plans. Every moment of "stay and wait" is an opportunity to surrender to God. Patience has a way of helping us dethrone ourselves from the center of our lives.

And suddenly there came from Heaven a sound like a mighty rushing wind, and it filled the entire house where they were sitting. And divided tongues as of fire appeared to them and rested on each one of them. And they were all filled with the Holy Spirit and began to speak in other tongues as the Spirit gave them utterance.
ACTS 2:2-4 ESV

Surrender always leads to a "suddenly." God makes us wait longer than we think He should, but then He surprises us in ways we never imagined He could. There it was, the power Jesus had promised had come in a miraculous encounter with God. It must have been a breathtaking, amazing experience. This power was so different than they thought it would be. Look at what happened as a result.

And at this sound the multitude came together, and they were bewildered, because each one was hearing them speak in his own language. And they were amazed and astonished, saying, "Are not all these who are speaking Galileans? And how is it that we hear, each of us in his own native language?"
ACTS 2:6-8 ESV

What just happened? Exactly what Jesus promised. These disciples received the gift of the Holy Spirit and immediately God used them as powerful, miraculous witnesses to the resurrection.

As Acts 2 continues, we read about how Peter boldly preached with conviction and passion. The disciple who, days before, couldn't stand up for Jesus in the face of a few, somehow convinced thousands to surrender their lives to Him. What happened to Peter? Peter had a new kind of power, the power to be a witness.

By the time Acts 2 ends, we see these same people now gathered in community, transformed by Jesus, full of compassion, encouraging one another, sharing one another's burdens, worshiping Jesus together, and meeting one another's needs "with glad and generous hearts." And what was the result? God added to their number daily. What happened to these people? They had a new kind of power, the power to be a witness.

What is a witness? A witness is someone who has met the *real* Jesus! A witness is someone who has surrendered their best-laid plans to Him. A witness is someone who has been empowered by the Holy Spirit to live a radically different kind of life. A witness is someone who freely forgives because they've been freely forgiven. A witness is someone who has been marked by God's grace. A witness is a community of people with a constellation of resources to love and serve and show compassion to the poor, the marginalized, and the weak. A witness is a community of people who give their lives away "with glad and generous hearts."

Jesus gives you the power to be a witness. Are you ready?

PERSONAL PRAYER TIME

This is a moment to be honest with yourself and with God. In light of everything you've read, what's on your heart?

BIBLE READING & MEDITATION

Grab a real paper Bible so that you can write in the margins, highlight verses, and make it your own. Read the following passages, meditate what you've read, and jot down your personal reflections.

DAY ONE

READ.

When they saw the courage of Peter and John and realized that they were unschooled, ordinary men, they were astonished and they took note that these men had been with Jesus.

ACTS 4:13 NIV

This is how we know that we live in Him and He in us: He has given us of His Spirit. And we have seen and testify that the Father has sent His Son to be the Savior of the world.

1 JOHN 4:13-14 NIV

REFLECT.

- What does this tell me about God?

- What does this tell me about myself?

- How would this change my life if I took it seriously?

WRITE.

DAY TWO

READ.

I know very well how foolish it sounds to those who are lost, when they hear that Jesus died to save them. But we who are saved recognize this message as the very power of God.

1 CORINTHIANS 1:18 TLB

Always be prepared to give an answer to everyone who asks you to give the reason for the hope that you have. But do this with gentleness and respect.

1 PETER 3:15 NIV

REFLECT.

- What does this tell me about God?

- What does this tell me about myself?

- How would this change my life if I took it seriously?

WRITE.

DAY THREE

READ.

I also pray that you will understand the incredible greatness of God's power for us who believe Him. This is the same mighty power that raised Christ from the dead and seated Him in the place of honor at God's right hand in the heavenly realms.

EPHESIANS 1:19-20 NLT

...and in Him are sharing the miracle of rising again to new life— and all this because you have faith in the tremendous power of God, who raised Christ from the dead.

COLOSSIANS 2:12 PHILLIPS

REFLECT.

- What does this tell me about God?

- What does this tell me about myself?

- How would this change my life if I took it seriously?

WRITE.

DAY FOUR

READ.

The weapons of our warfare are not physical [weapons of flesh and blood]. Our weapons are divinely powerful for the destruction of fortresses.

2 CORINTHIANS 10:4 AMP

"My grace is all you need, for My power is greatest when you are weak." I am most happy, then, to be proud of my weaknesses, in order to feel the protection of Christ's power over me. I am content with weaknesses, insults, hardships, persecutions, and difficulties for Christ's sake. For when I am weak, then I am strong.

2 CORINTHIANS 12:8-10 GNT

REFLECT.

- What does this tell me about God?
- What does this tell me about myself?
- How would this change my life if I took it seriously?

WRITE.

DAY FIVE

READ.

*Peter stood up with the eleven apostles and shouted to the crowd.
"Listen carefully, my fellow Jews and residents of Jerusalem. You
need to clearly understand what's happening here."*

*"Can't you see it? God has resurrected Jesus, and we all have seen
Him! Then God exalted Him to His right hand upon the throne
of highest honor. And the Father gave Him the authority to send
the promised Holy Spirit, which is being poured out upon us today.
This is what you're seeing and hearing!"*

*Peter preached to them and warned them with these words:
"Be rescued from the wayward and perverse culture of this world!"
Those who believed the word that day numbered three thousand.
They were all baptized and added to the church."*

ACTS 2:14, 32-33, 40-41 TPT

REFLECT.

- What does this tell me about God?

- What does this tell me about myself?

- How would this change my life if I took it seriously?

WRITE.

GROUP TIME

OPENING THOUGHTS

After a time of introductions or catching up, open with prayer and give everyone an opportunity to share their thoughts on this week's topic.

Use the Big Idea and Starter Questions below to open discussion and encourage people to reflect on their Pre-Group study. An easy way to do that is to ask about personal observations, pressing questions, or unique insights from this week's study.

GROWING CONNECTED

THE BIG IDEA

Jesus gives you power to be a witness.

STARTER QUESTIONS

1. What embarrassing things do some Christians do in the name of sharing their faith?

2. Have you ever had an awkward experience trying to share your faith? Tell us about it!

3. Have you had someone from a different faith try to evangelize you? How did you feel?

4. If you're a Christian, tell us how the person who shared their faith with you led you to Christ.

VIDEO TEACHING

Write down any thoughts or ideas that stand out to you.

GROUP DISCUSSION

Use the following questions to promote healthy discussion of this week's video.

DISCUSSION QUESTIONS

1. What are your greatest ambitions?

2. In what ways does Jesus shape your view of power?

3. Have you experienced a moment where your world was turned upside down? What happened?

4. What does it mean to you to be a witness?

GROUP PRAYER TIME

Open up the floor for prayer requests. Pray for your group as a whole and for any individual requests.

PRAYER REQUESTS

NEXT STEPS

After prayerful consideration and healthy, candid discussion, let's apply what we've learned. Use this week's Personal Challenge and Helpful Questions to help you identify your next steps spiritually.

GROUP CHALLENGE

Ask God to show you the areas of your heart that need resurrection. Ask Him to help you surrender those areas to Jesus.

The new community of Christians at the end Acts 2 is a remarkable community. They learned with one another, ate with one another, prayed for one another, took care of one another's needs, and shared everything with one another "with glad and generous hearts." That just sounds fun, doesn't it?

Instead of a Personal Challenge, this week we have a Group Challenge for you. It's called "One Another One Another." No Helpful Questions are needed. This one is easy!

NEXT STEPS EXERCISE
ONE ANOTHER ONE ANOTHER

Your assignment is to set a time to get together over the next few weeks and do some kind of activity as a group! Go bowling, ride Go-Karts, play miniature golf, go to a movie, go out to eat, play cards, play board games, have a barbecue, or whatever you like.

Choose the activity together and decide right now to be all-in. This is an opportunity to celebrate what God has done in your lives together and experience the joys of community. We're all busy. Make this a priority. You and the people in your group deserve it.

Enjoy yourselves!

REAL PURPOSE

PRE-GROUP

THE BIG IDEA

Jesus didn't just save you *from* something, He saved you *for* something.

GO THEREFORE.

"Go therefore and make disciples of all the nations, baptizing them in the name of the Father and of the Son and of the Holy Spirit, teaching them to observe all things that I have commanded you; and lo, I am with you always, even to the end of the age."
MATTHEW 28:19-20 NKJV

One of the amazing things about Jesus was just how approachable He was. Whether you were a devoted disciple, a skeptical Pharisee, a Roman centurion, or unsightly leper, Jesus welcomed you. Whether you were a shrewd tax collector, a greedy rich person, a guilty prostitute, or a desperate paraplegic, Jesus invited you to come close.

"Come and see" was a call to experience intimate closeness with God, to be rescued, to be healed, to become whole in His presence. No one who encountered Jesus had ever met anyone like Him. How could He be so powerful and so holy and yet so humble and so touchable? The invitation to follow Jesus is an invitation to be close.

Still more surprising than Jesus' compelling call to come close was His bold commission to go far! When you meet the *real* Jesus, He saves you from your sin, but not just for salvation's sake. He makes you whole, but not just so you can be holy. Jesus always frees you so He can use you. "Come and see" inevitably leads to "go and tell."

Just before His arrest, Jesus told His disciples that they would all abandon Him in some way. It was not just Peter and Judas who betrayed Him. Most of the others fled and hid. (See Matthew 26:31-33)

What must it have been like after the resurrection to find out Jesus wanted to see them? What must it have felt like to have embraced Him again? To not only see His wounds, but to touch them? To not only be in His presence, but to talk with Him and share meals with Him? In full view of their brokenness, Jesus invited them close.

Then consider what a shock it must have been to hear these words:

"All authority in Heaven and Earth has been given to Me. Go therefore into all nations..."

Did He know what He was doing? Many of these people had abandoned Him. They weren't ready! They weren't educated enough, influential enough, or bold enough. They didn't have the resources or the experience they needed. Did He really have the audacity to look into the eyes of His flawed, imperfect followers and say "go be My representatives to the world"? Only Jesus could do such a thing. His closeness was designed to show the power of His grace. His commission was meant to elicit their dependence on Him.

If you've been close to Jesus, are you ready to go? If not, don't worry. Jesus didn't just save you from something, He saved you for something. Go, therefore.

COME, SEE.

"Come, see a man who told me everything I ever did. Could this be the Messiah?"

JOHN 4:29 NIV

"Go, therefore" is a call to compel other people to "come, see." It's a call to introduce people to the *real* Jesus.

John chapter 4 gives us the story of a woman in Samaria who encountered Jesus. As she approached a village water well, she saw Jesus sitting next to it. To her surprise Jesus spoke to her. Samaritans believed in the God of Israel, but because they were not Jews by birth, most Jews viewed Samaritans as second-class citizens spiritually. In addition, women in general were not highly esteemed in society. Jesus was not only a man, He was a Jewish man. And not only was He a Jew, He was a Rabbi. From the outside looking in, the cultural chasm between these two people seemed to be enormous. Simply by speaking to her, Jesus shattered cultural categories.

Jesus not only spoke to her, He asked her to give Him some of the water she was about to draw from the well. For a Jew to make such a request of a Samaritan was unthinkable. Anything a Samaritan touched was automatically considered unclean.

In the 1960's several local municipalities in the southern part of the United States enacted what they referred to as "separate but equal" racial segregation laws. Blacks and whites were given separate education opportunities, separate public transportation, and even separate public restrooms. "Whites Only" signs could be seen on business windows, above water fountains, and on public swimming pool gates.

In 1961 in Nashville, Tennessee, two young black men decided to go for a swim in one of the public "Whites Only" pools. Oh the uproar that ensued! Every public pool in town was drained and shut down indefinitely. It was as if the white elites thought black people were somehow going to contaminate them. "Separate but equal" was definitely not equal. More than half a century later, this seems unconscionable. But it was reality. And marginalized people all over the world have experienced this kind of reality for centuries.

Informed by life experience, the Samaritan woman expected this kind of prejudice from Jesus, the Jewish Rabbi. "What about your cleanliness laws, Rabbi?" she must have thought. Little did she know, Jesus was not just a Jewish Rabbi, He was Savior to all mankind. Yes, even Samaritans. He didn't care about cultural expectations. He cared about her. He invited her close, looked into her troubled heart, and offered her true peace. In one brief conversation, Jesus changed this woman's life.

She immediately left her water jar and ran into the city. "Come, see a man who told me everything I ever did. Could this be the Messiah?" Her "go" was also a "come and see," pointing people to Jesus. So compelling was her invitation that "many Samaritans believed in Him…"

Jesus wants to speak to your troubles, then send you to the troubled. He wants to heal your wounds, then send you to the wounded. He wants to quiet your anxieties and quench your thirsty soul so you can lead people to His still waters.

Could this be our Messiah? Come, see.

NOTES

BIBLE READING & MEDITATION

Grab a real paper Bible so that you can write in the margins, highlight verses, and make it your own. Read the following passages, meditate what you've read, and jot down your personal reflections.

DAY ONE

READ.

"For I know the plans I have for you, declares the Lord, plans for welfare and not for evil, to give you a future and a hope."
JEREMIAH 29:11 ESV

Therefore, my beloved brothers, be steadfast, immovable, always abounding in the work of the Lord, knowing that in the Lord your labor is not in vain.
1 CORINTHIANS 15:58 ESV

REFLECT.

- What does this tell me about God?

- What does this tell me about myself?

- How would this change my life if I took it seriously?

WRITE.

DAY TWO

READ.

And I am sure of this, that He who began a good work in you will bring it to completion at the day of Jesus Christ.

PHILIPPIANS 1:6 ESV

But it is just as the Scriptures say, "What God has planned for people who love Him is more than eyes have seen or ears have heard. It has never even entered our minds!" God's Spirit has shown you everything. His Spirit finds out everything, even what is deep in the mind of God.

1 CORINTHIANS 2:9-10 CEV

REFLECT.

- What does this tell me about God?
- What does this tell me about myself?
- How would this change my life if I took it seriously?

WRITE.

DAY THREE

READ.

He comforts us in all our troubles so that we can comfort others. When they are troubled, we will be able to give them the same comfort God has given us.

2 CORINTHIANS 1:4 NLT

And we know that all things work together for good to those who love God, to those who are called according to His purpose.

ROMANS 8:28 NKJV

REFLECT.

- What does this tell me about God?

- What does this tell me about myself?

- How would this change my life if I took it seriously?

WRITE.

DAY FOUR

READ.

For we are His workmanship, created in Christ Jesus for good works, which God prepared beforehand, that we should walk in them.

EPHESIANS 2:10 ESV

Many are the plans in the mind of a man, but it is the purpose of the Lord that will stand.

PROVERBS 19:21 ESV

REFLECT.

- What does this tell me about God?
- What does this tell me about myself?
- How would this change my life if I took it seriously?

WRITE.

DAY FIVE

READ.

*Yes, and I will rejoice… as it is my eager expectation and hope
that I will not be at all ashamed, but that with full courage no
as always Christ will be honored in my body, whether by life
or by death. For to me to live is Christ, and to die is gain.*

PHILIPPIANS 1:18B, 20-21 ESV

*One who cleanses himself from these things will be a vessel
for honor, sanctified, fit for the Master's use, and prepared
for every good work.*

2 TIMOTHY 2:21 MEV

REFLECT.

- What does this tell me about God?
- What does this tell me about myself?
- How would this change my life if I took it seriously?

WRITE.

GROUP TIME

OPENING THOUGHTS

After a time of introductions or catching up, open with prayer and give everyone an opportunity to share their thoughts on this week's topic.

Use The Big Idea and Starter Questions to open discussion and encourage people to reflect on their Pre-Group study. Ask about personal observations, pressing questions, or unique insights from this week's study.

GROWING CONNECTED

THE BIG IDEA

Jesus didn't just save you *from* something, He saved you *for* something.

STARTER QUESTIONS

1. Describe the person you know who seems to be closest to God. What gives you that impression?

2. Talk about someone you know who seems to be living out their God-given purpose.

3. What kinds of things can keep a person from living out their full purpose?

VIDEO TEACHING

Write down any thoughts or ideas that stand out to you from this week's teaching.

DISCUSSION QUESTIONS

1. What is something you love to do that also helps other people? How is that related to your purpose?

2. If you had to guess, what would you say God saved you for?

3. Can you think of any examples of people who are helping others with the very thing God rescued them from?

4. Do you feel close to Jesus right now?
    Why or why not?

5. Do you feel prepared to be used by God?
    Why or why not?

GROUP PRAYER TIME

Open up the floor for prayer requests. Pray for your group as a whole and for any individual requests.

PRAYER REQUESTS

NEXT STEPS

Often what God rescues you from is what He wants to use you for. We are not where we will be, but let's celebrate how God's grace has rescued us from where we once were. Author Paul David Tripp once said, "No one is more influential in your life than you are. Because no one talks to you more than you do." Re-hearing what God has done in your life can be a powerful catalyst for more growth. With that in mind, we have a special exercise for you this week.

Your personal challenge is called "My Spiritual Story." Your assignment is simple, but not easy—write your spiritual story in less than 500 words (1-2 pages). Focus on God's grace and how it has intersected your life. In fact, make the title of your spiritual story "My Grace Journey."

There are no Helpful Questions to guide you this week because there's no right or wrong way to do this. Be honest about your current struggles, encourage yourself with memories of God's grace, and write it down.

Happy writing!

NEXT STEPS EXERCISE
MY GRACE JOURNEY

REAL FREEDOM

PRE-GROUP

THE BIG IDEA
Real freedom is a progressive journey.

WHAT IF MORE IS POSSIBLE?
For my determined purpose is that I may know Him, that I may progressively become more deeply and intimately acquainted with Him, perceiving and recognizing and understanding the wonders of His Person more strongly and more clearly.
PHILIPPIANS 3:10 AMPC

Freedom is not a check box we can mark off our list. We all want to be free from our past, free to live like Jesus. But real freedom is progressive. And there's joy in the journey.

We started our Real Jesus journey together with the words of John, the disciple Jesus loved. "Jesus is God." John professed that there was so much more to Jesus than even he imagined.

Over the last several weeks we have investigated this truth for ourselves. As we've looked at the words and individual encounters with Him, what have you experienced personally? Do you see Jesus differently than you did before? Have you discovered the depths of His grace? Would you say you've met the *real* Jesus?

No matter your answer, our next question to you is the same: What if more is possible? What if Jesus is still bigger than you think He is? Still better than you think He is? More loving than you think He is? More gracious than you think He is?

What if your Real Jesus journey has only just begun? That's our hope for you. We hope you'll determine to "progressively become more deeply and intimately acquainted" with Jesus for the rest of your life. That's an invitation to freedom. No matter how close or how distant you feel, Jesus invites you to come closer.

WHEN TROUBLE COMES.

"I have told you all this so that you may find your peace in Me. You will find trouble in the world—but, never lose heart, I have conquered the world!"
JOHN 16:33 PHILLIPS

Please know this: you have a spiritual enemy who doesn't want you to be close to God. Many of the temptations that have led you away from God in your past, many of the troubles that have come at you through various circumstances, and many of the hurts that have weighed you down, were set in motion by your enemy. In this world you will have trouble, because you do have an adversary.

Casting all your care upon Him, for He cares for you. Be sober, be vigilant; because your adversary the devil walks about like a roaring lion, seeking whom he may devour. Resist him, steadfast in the faith, knowing that the same sufferings are experienced by your brotherhood in the world.
1 PETER 5:7-9 NKJV

Resist trouble. When it comes your way, remember Jesus. His resurrection means you can live with supernatural peace no matter what trouble comes. His ascension into Heaven means there's more to His plans than you think.

At the end of his life, John, the disciple Jesus loved, found himself exiled on an island called Patmos. John had lived a long life and had seen so much. In addition to having seen the crucifixion and resurrection of Jesus, John had likely seen the destruction of Jerusalem and literally thousands of crucifixions of his people along the way. He had outlived his fellow disciples, seeing many of them hunted down, tortured, and killed.

Before he died, John had some amazing prophetic visions. With all of the trouble he had seen in mind, he wrote down those visions to challenge and encourage followers of Jesus in the book of Revelation.

In Revelation 21 John shares the vision he had of seeing a future Jesus in "a new Heaven and a new Earth" (verse 1). Through the words of John's vision, Jesus gives us a glimpse into the hope of our future in Him.

He will wipe away every tear from their eyes, and death shall be no more, neither shall there be mourning, nor crying, nor pain anymore, for the former things have passed away.
REVELATION 21:4 ESV

Only Jesus can make such a promise. Will you lean in to His promises when trouble comes? Knowing the resources He offers should allow you to loosen your grip on the fleeting pleasures and the beckoning distractions of here and now. Knowing there will be no more pain allows you to face the pains of a life of surrender with joy. Knowing that the former things will pass away allows you to face your yesterdays with grace and truth.

No matter what happens in the next few weeks and months, trust that Jesus really is as good as He says He is. Trust that He really does care about the smallest details of your life. He'll never leave you or forsake you. He wants you close.

Real freedom is a progressive journey, and wherever your journey with Jesus takes you, know that there's joy in the journey!

NOTES

NOTES

BIBLE READING & MEDITATION

Grab a real paper Bible so that you can write in the margins, highlight verses, and make it your own. Read the following passages, meditate what you've read, and jot down your personal reflections.

DAY ONE

READ.

My brethren, count it all joy when you fall into various trials, knowing that the testing of your faith produces patience. But let patience have its perfect work, that you may be perfect and complete, lacking nothing. If any of you lacks wisdom, let him ask of God, Who gives to all liberally and without reproach, and it will be given to him.

JAMES 1:2-5 NKJV

REFLECT.

- What does this tell me about God?

- What does this tell me about myself?

- How would this change my life if I took it seriously?

WRITE.

DAY TWO

READ.

Where can I go from Your Spirit? Or where can I flee from Your presence? If I ascend into Heaven, You are there; If I make my bed in hell, behold, You are there. If I take the wings of the morning, And dwell in the uttermost parts of the sea, Even there Your hand shall lead me, And Your right hand shall hold me.

PSALM 139:7-10 NKJV

REFLECT.

- What does this tell me about God?

- What does this tell me about myself?

- How would this change my life if I took it seriously?

WRITE.

DAY THREE

READ.

*Is anyone crying for help? God is listening, ready to rescue you.
If your heart is broken, you'll find God right there; if you're kicked
in the gut, He'll help you catch your breath. Disciples so often get
into trouble; still, God is there every time.*

PSALM 34:17-19 MSG

REFLECT.

- What does this tell me about God?

- What does this tell me about myself?

- How would this change my life if I took it seriously?

WRITE.

DAY FOUR

READ.

But thanks be to God, Who gives us the victory through our Lord Jesus Christ. Therefore, my beloved brothers, be steadfast, immovable, always abounding in the work of the Lord, knowing that in the Lord your labor is not in vain.

1 CORINTHIANS 15:57-58 ESV

REFLECT.

- What does this tell me about God?

- What does this tell me about myself?

- How would this change my life if I took it seriously?

WRITE.

DAY FIVE

READ.

When I saw Him, I fell at His feet as if I were dead. But He laid His right hand on me and said, "Don't be afraid! I am the First and the Last. I am the living one. I died, but look—I am alive forever and ever! And I hold the keys of death and the grave."

REVELATION 1:17-18 NLT

REFLECT.

- What does this tell me about God?
- What does this tell me about myself?
- How would this change my life if I took it seriously?

WRITE.

GROUP TIME

OPENING THOUGHTS

After a time of introductions or catching up, open with prayer and give everyone an opportunity to share their thoughts on this week's topic.

Use The Big Idea and Starter Questions to open discussion and encourage people to reflect on their Pre-Group study. Ask about personal observations, pressing questions, or unique insights from this week's study.

GROWING CONNECTED

THE BIG IDEA

Real freedom is a progressive journey.

STARTER QUESTIONS

1. Have you or someone you know ever overcome a major addiction? Describe what freedom looked like in that situation.

2. Talk about someone you know whose life has dramatically changed after meeting the *real* Jesus.

3. Take a moment to celebrate the steps, big or small, that you've seen in someone's life here in this group.

VIDEO TEACHING

Write down any thoughts or ideas that stand out to you from this week's teaching.

DISCUSSION QUESTIONS

1. In just a few words, reflect on your personal Real Jesus journey these last several weeks. Talk about some of the moments you're most grateful for.

2. Take a moment to celebrate someone who made a significant impact on your Real Jesus journey this semester.

3. If freedom is a progressive journey of grace, what are some hopes and dreams you're working toward in the future?

4. If it's true that our Real Jesus journey has just begun, what are your next steps?

GROUP PRAYER TIME

Open up the floor for prayer requests. Pray for your group as a whole and for any individual requests.

PRAYER REQUESTS

NEXT STEPS

One of the ways God leads us and protects us is through relationships. This group is meant to provide relationships for you beyond the 10 weeks of this study. As this season comes to an end, commit to praying for the people in your group on a regular basis.

Your exercise is just to write the names of the people in your group and pray for them this week and maybe beyond. What do you pray? Pray that they continue to find the freedom and pursue Jesus more deeply and intimately wherever they are.

NEXT STEPS EXERCISE

MY REAL JESUS GROUP

Date:

_____

Names: Numbers:

_____   _____

_____   _____

_____   _____

_____   _____

_____   _____

_____   _____

_____   _____

_____   _____

_____   _____

_____   _____

_____   _____

REAL JESUS

RESOURCES

REAL STORIES

A word fitly spoken is like apples of gold in a setting of silver.
PROVERBS 25:11 ESV

We have found that one of the most uplifting things that can happen on a Real Jesus journey is to hear from someone who's had a similar story to yours. Here are a few Real Jesus Stories that we believe will encourage you, inspire you, and challenge you to keep pursuing Jesus with all of your heart.

NICOLE'S STORY

I have found **freedom**!

My journey has looked like this… I am a 34-year-old woman who is a Christian. I attend church, have a small group, and a beautiful life as a wife and mother. That's how things look on the outside. On the inside, Satan was winning the battle in my life almost every single day.

My biggest enemy has been lies Satan told me every day that I believed. As odd as it sounds, I probably spent more time listening to the voice of those lies than I did to the voice of God. Here's a snippet of what I heard throughout the day. Every day.

"You are an orphan, not worthy of love…"
"You are a failure…"
"You will fail your children like your parents
failed you…"
"You can't be loved, you are broken…"
"You are a sinner…"
"You will end up just like your mother…"
"You are ugly…"
"You will be abandoned…"

It seemed like I heard these lies no matter how much I prayed or how much I attended church. I knew God was good but I didn't understand what it meant to be accepted as one of His children. I didn't feel worthy of that kind of love, so I continued to listen to the lies. The situations that caused these lies to be so prevalent were things that happened in my past, that were beyond my control. They were intended to hurt me then. They continued to hurt me for years.

As a kid, my home was unstable. My father committed suicide. I lived with a single mom who was abusive. She was an addict. My half-brothers became addicts. One was in prison by age 18.

At age 14, I was removed from my home by DHS, placed at a shelter, then moved to a children's home. By the time I was 18 I was completely lost and at my darkest place. I had no family of my own and the burden of a generational sin that almost destroyed me.

Things started to make a turn for the better. I met my husband and we started a family. I loved my life. My life was finally happy. I felt blessed. This is what I wanted. But I wasn't free. I was still me.

Why did I spend so much time seeking words of affirmation? I needed to be affirmed to feel loved or to feel a glimpse of feeling worthy. Maybe words of affirmation would quiet the voice telling me lies every day. I wanted the outside to look perfect because I feared the daily inside struggles I faced would be exposed.

Through growing close to my small group and diving deeper into God's word over the past few semesters, it is as though layers of pain have been shed. It started last semester as I was struggling to balance my career and my family. I felt unworthy as things were falling off my plate daily.

If I ever wanted freedom I had to be willing to accept God's love... but I just didn't know how to do that. Then I had a revelation. I realized I was seeking words of affirmation from my family to feel worthy, when the only affirmation I needed was already written in God's word. I needed to learn how to believe His words.

I actually wrote myself a letter as though it were my Heavenly Father writing to me. It was in that moment I felt love, I saw the *real* Jesus love me. I felt free! From then on, I read the Bible differently. I realized His promises are not just for my children. They are for me. He left the 99 for me.

Now the voice I hear throughout my day is God whispering His promises to me. I went from just being happy to knowing about God to finding the freedom of knowing God's love. His love didn't change, but I finally learned how to accept it.

LISA'S STORY

I grew up in a Christian home. We always went to church and I always did what I was supposed to do. I never went through a "rebellious" stage. Other people's stories involve becoming free from addiction, overcoming rejection, or losing a family member. My story always felt so simple and ordinary. I just had an ordinary life.

That's all great on the outside, but I didn't realize there were some major changes that needed to take place in my heart. God had a deeper story for me, I just needed to get to a place of humility to even see it.

One of my biggest problems in my life, especially as a Christian, is that I was so good at self-deception. I told myself I have good intentions and went through life never realizing I was just deceiving myself.

"I may have some minor issues because, as a human, we all have some shortcomings, but I'm not as bad as so-and-so." This was the kind of lie I told myself.

I made a choice to seek God, really seek Him. As I was reading my Bible I came across a scripture that says "man thinks his ways are pure, but God looks at the heart."

I asked God about this. "What am I doing that I think is good, but I'm only deceiving myself?" He didn't answer right away, but over time He began to show me how selfish I really was.

I started to realize I based so much of who I was after what I did (my performance). I had a Pharisee/judgmental attitude toward other people and I never even realized it.

It was self-deception. It was pride, the very carbon monoxide of sin. It was hidden and it was deadly. It was slowly killing me and I didn't even know it. I thank Jesus for saving me from myself.

I've always dealt with insecurity since my preteen years (at least). I decided I needed to deal with this area of my life. I asked God why I was so insecure, indecisive, un opinionated, etc.… He showed me the following:

God gave me a quiet personality. At some point, I started accepting lies from Satan. Because of that, the "pure" or "good" in that personality slowly began to be warped.

I went from being quiet (which was God's gift to me) to being shy (which is a fear-based label).

I've heard it said that you become what you believe about yourself. This is what happened to me. The lies I accepted became part of me. Satan would fuel that fire with situations and real-life events to "prove" those lies.

One of the lies was that I was "forgettable," thinking that's how others saw me. So I had become forgettable. Another lie was that I didn't "bring anything to the table." So I stopped bringing my opinions and ideas.

Other lies included, "Do these people want to be my friend or are we only friends because of my other friends or my husband?" Or, "Am I even fun? Do people care if I'm even here?" Today, I can see the root cause of those thoughts. My identity was not in Jesus.

I was not walking in freedom. I thought I knew freedom in Jesus. Had I been addicted to fear? Self-pity? Low self-worth? Was it so normal that I didn't even know I was a prisoner to it? How could I not tell?

It's because of self-deception. Today, I'm slowly learning to walk in the real freedom God has for me.

"Therefore, if anyone is in Christ, he is a new creation; old things have passed away and look, new things have come."
2 CORINTHIANS 5:17 HCSB

CASEY'S STORY

Lies the enemy tells me:

> *"You are your father's daughter.*
> *You leave when it gets hard just like he did.*
>
> *You are your father's daughter.*
> *You'll be an adulterer just like him.*
>
> *You are your father's daughter.*
> *You've got to survive like him."*

Trapped. That's how I felt.

Unable to make it better but still willing to try with every last ounce of energy I could muster. Why didn't my dad understand how crazy he seemed? He was leaving us. He sat there, stone-faced. The pastor of the church before my parents took over held him and sobbed. It wasn't just a marriage he was walking away from for another woman, it wasn't just his children or his home, it was his calling and everything we knew. All the ideas we had about who God was and how life was supposed to be were shattered.

I wanted to feel something, anything. Maybe pain could wake me up and maybe my family would wake up too? I offered to be the punching bag for my mother's grief while my sisters offered comfort. Why? It was easier to accept pain than offer love.

I think deep down I thought, "I don't belong here with these weak people." I remember one night things were especially volatile and I was determined to get out. My siblings all piled on top of me so I couldn't leave. Buried under their sobbing bodies I pleaded, "Just let me go. I have to get out." I'd never thought about how they might not be able to handle someone else walking out on them. I finally got to the back door and my brother, in an effort to stop me, slammed it on my fingers... hard. And immediately I was strong again. "It's okay. I'm fine." I spoke in reassuring tones. "I think you may have broken my finger but I'm not sure. Will you get me a towel?" Immediately swollen and bloody. Finally, outward proof of how I felt inside. This whole thing just hurts.

That was the first moment in my life the genuineness of my faith would be deeply tested. Seeking God in the numbness, in survival mode, in crisis felt like my only option. It felt like I had nowhere else to go. But I didn't feel Him. I didn't hear Him. No matter how hard I listened, no matter how hard I cried. It's as if He stood in the room watching my tears soak the carpet. Not with an ounce of malicious intent did He withhold any feeling, but He did it with purpose. He let me sink deep into the sorrow and the grief, but there was never once despair. I knew He was there. But I couldn't feel Him. But I told Him, "I know You're there. I know You hear me. I'm Yours. If I never feel Your presence again, I'm Yours." It was there that I learned to abide. He wasn't going to leave like my dad had, like I wanted to.

Faith was not what so many people had tried to convince me it was. If that was the case, my sister would be six feet tall because she prayed, had "faith," and wanted to be the best volleyball player she could. She's 5'6" and a missionary. He just doesn't do things the way we think He should. Faith is what God uses to make us more like Jesus. It's radical trust and utter dependence.

Hebrews 11:1 calls it the assurance of hope and the substance of things not seen. Isn't it interesting how when we talk about people of "substance" what we usually mean is their character?

These seasons of deep brokenness have been the most transformational moments of my life. I wouldn't trade them for anything. And yes, I said seasons with an "s". These seasons came on the heels of what felt like monumental heartbreak but most recently it has come following a step of faith towards something I've felt called to since I was a child.

The enemy tells me, "You don't deserve that. You're a fraud. You are your father's daughter."

I found myself in a panic, feeling like the thing I would be over the moon to have is so far and so impossible, and as always, just out of reach.

Lost hope. Despair. Shame.

Then, like the faithful, loving, patient God He is, He whispers, "Let Me be enough."

What do I believe? Is Jesus enough? Do I want Him or the feelings? Do I want God or the job? Do I want Yahweh or the chance to make a name for myself? When I tell the great I Am, the all-sufficient One, that He's all I want, He gives me the opportunity to walk it out.

He stood beside me again as I wept. I allowed myself to feel the sorrow. Normally, I would find a way out. A way to resolve any cognitive dissonance I may have. Some platitude about what "God showed me" would help me get through the day. But not this time. This time He's teaching me something. Purging, excavating, refining. And instead of running, I'm staying.

I know what He's doing in me will reap a harvest of joy. But I don't submit to this work for joy that's a mere feeling of contentment or well-being. I submit to this work because He is my Joy. He is my delight and my great reward. He has pledged Himself to me and I to Him.

I am His inheritance. And He has taken the shame that has threatened to stifle my hope and exchanged it for radiance.

I am my father's daughter, but shame is not my inheritance.

How do I know? It's simple. I decided to look up.

Those who look to Him are radiant, and their faces shall never be ashamed.
PSALM 34:5 ESV

BOOK
RECOMMENDATIONS

KNOW YOURSELF THAT YOU MAY KNOW GOD

This is eternal life, that they know You, the only true God,
and Jesus Christ Whom You have sent.

JOHN 17:3 ESV

One of the ways you can tell you're on a Real Jesus journey is you have a sincere thirst for more God. You want to know Him more deeply, more progressively, more intimately. If you're on this pursuit, understand two things. First, you will never fully quench your thirst for knowing God. Second, the quest itself is profoundly satisfying.

One of the things we have found in our own personal Real Jesus journeys around Church on the Move is this—you can't meet the *real* Jesus until you face the real you. Augustine said it this way in his book Confessions, "How can you draw close to God when you are far from your own self?"

Over the years we found so many blogs, articles, podcasts, videos, and books that have been invaluable on our individual quests to "know ourselves that we may know God." We couldn't possibly recount all of those resources, but we do have a few books we would love to recommend for your journey (in no particular order).

Jesus the King by Timothy Keller

The Prodigal God by Timothy Keller

Waking the Dead by John Eldredge

Out of the Saltshaker by Rebecca Manley Pippert

Finding I Am by Lysa TerKeurst

Jesus Outside the Lines by Scott Sauls

Knowing God by J.I. Packer

Basic Christianity by John Stott

Emotionally Healthy Spirituality by Peter Scazzero

The Great Divorce by C.S. Lewis

Mere Christianity by C.S. Lewis

Instruments in the Redeemer's Hands by Paul David Tripp

Good or God? by John Bevere

Abide in Christ by Andrew Murray

The Knowledge of the Holy by A.W. Tozer